# Our Nation's Heritage

# OUR NATION'S HERITAGE

EDITED BY

*J. B. Priestley*

AUTHOR OF 'THE GOOD COMPANIONS'

J. M. DENT AND SONS LTD
BEDFORD ST LONDON W.C.2.

BOOK
PRODUCTION
WAR ECONOMY
STANDARD

# Contents

*The publishers are indebted to Mr J. E. Hales for his assistance in the selection of material for this book.*

# Illustrations

# Introduction

When we think of romantic and beautiful islands, we think of places like Tahiti in the South Seas and Trinidad in the Caribbean Sea. And certainly these are romantic and beautiful islands, as I know quite well, for I have stayed on them. What we forget, however, is that we live on a romantic and beautiful island too, the isle of Britain. In ancient days, the times of the Carthaginians and Phoenicians and Romans, Britain was regarded as a very romantic, strange, magical place, where all manner of misty enchantments might happen, on the very edge of the world. Even now if you see Stonehenge on the right sort of day, with a green haze over Salisbury Plain, you will understand why our country seemed so strange to these people from the Mediterranean, where everything is bright and clear-cut. The secret of Britain is simply that it is really a small island. It has a great variety of landscape packed into comparatively little space. It has the sea always round the corner. Even in the Midlands, the sea is not really far away. I have travelled through nearly all the Middle-Western states of America, and there sometimes the sea is nearly fifteen hundred miles away, so far away that millions of people have never set eyes on it, and you feel the difference at once and know quite well that you are land-locked. Nowhere in our country can you really feel land-locked. The sea is not far away and it is all round us, like a vast, misty window.

This mistiness, now, is important. You have to go abroad and live there for some time before you realize, on returning, that the landscape of Britain is nearly always covered with at least a light haze. This prevents us from enjoying very bright sunshine, but on the other hand it gives our hills and

*valleys an exquisite softness, so that instead of everything
standing out sharply, one thing melts into another, almost like
the strange places we see in dreams. This makes our country
a fine one for poets to describe. It also explains why nearly
all our most successful landscape artists have painted in
water-colours, in which you can obtain the melting effect, and
not in oils. When you have a chance, look at pictures done
by the water-colour artists who worked during the period
1780–1820, such men as Girtin, Turner, Cotman, Crome,
Cox. And these men were very fortunate because the England
they wandered about in (they were great wanderers—lucky
fellows!) and painted so beautifully had not then been spoilt.
Nearly everything they saw then was enchanting, magic
island stuff. You catch glimpses of that older and unspoilt
England in some of the poems and essays in this book. And
let me warn you that there is not much of this unspoilt, magic
country left.*

*Nevertheless, unless you have the bad luck to live in the very
worst parts of the Black Country or one of the mining districts,
you are never really very far away from some magic bit of this
older Britain. Any day you may jump out of a bus or train
somewhere and see one of these precious bits of enchanted
countryside, like something from a Shakespeare play or a
poem by Wordsworth, still glimmering in our queer, hazy
sunlight. To my mind, that sunlight plays on many of the
pages of this book. You see, what an author does, whether he
writes in verse or prose, is to try and tell you, in exact and
vivid detail, just what went on in his mind. You know how,
after you have returned from a day's outing somewhere, your
mother or father or older sister or somebody interested in you
will ask, 'What was it like?' Well, what was it like? If it
was a good day, there is in your mind a sort of terrific shining
jumble, and you try to find words to explain that jumble—the
excitement of starting out, the light on the fields, the winking
of bright water in the streams, the splashing in the pools, the
taste of the sandwiches, the green Robin Hood shadows deep*

n the woods, the smell of the grass, the nice tiredness of evening
—and so on and so on and so on.    It is an exciting but rather
desperate business, this of trying to explain what it was like.
Well, that is what authors are doing, and have been doing for
thousands of years.

Here they are trying to tell you what our island was like:
the grass and the trees; the birds (and this is a famous island
for birds); the places you come to and the places you leave;
the folk, all manner of odd folk, you come across; the great
adventure of living on this island.    If you read properly,
that is, letting every word soak in, so to speak, getting the
taste and colour of everything described, and not racing and
gabbling through, you will enjoy what they enjoyed, and be
given magical eyes and ears so that you can see and hear both
through space and time.    This is what good reading can do
for you, turning you into a sort of wizard who is at least two
thousand years old and yet can hop about wherever he pleases.
Wireless is wonderful, just turning a switch and having music
and jokes poured out for you.    But this business of writing
and reading, which has been going on a long time now, is
more wonderful still.    The films are a marvel, for there, in the
sudden darkness, people pop up and laugh and talk.    But
literature is still more marvellous.    Imagine staring at a map
until it became alive, with cloud shadows floating across the
hills, the grass waving in the fields, and people working and
playing all over the place.    That is what really happens in
this book, if you read it in the proper way.    The mysterious
and beautiful isle of Albion, which those brown, hook-nosed
sailors of ancient times saw looming whitely through the mists,
becomes alive, and you yourself are part of its magic.

J. B. PRIESTLEY

# 1. Farming

L. Farming

# The Mowing of a Field

NEXT morning, before it was yet broad day, I awoke, and thought of the mowing. The birds were already chattering in the trees beside my window, all except the nightingale, which had left and flown away to the Weald, where he sings all summer by day as well as by night in the oaks and the hazel spinneys, and especially along the little river Adur, one of the rivers of the Weald. The birds and the thought of the mowing had awakened me, and I went down the stairs and along the stone floors to where I could find a scythe; and when I took it from its nail, I remembered how, fourteen years ago, I had last gone out with my scythe, just so, into the fields at morning. In between that day and this were many things, cities, and armies, and a confusion of books, mountains and the desert, and horrible great breadths of sea.

When I got out into the long grass the sun was not yet risen, but there were already many colours in the eastern sky, and I made haste to sharpen my scythe, so that I might get to the cutting before the dew should dry. Some say that it is best to wait till all the dew has risen, so as to get the grass quite dry from the very first. But, though it is an advantage to get the grass quite dry, yet it is not worth while to wait till the dew has risen. For, in the first place, you lose many hours of work (and those the coolest), and next—which is more important—you lose that great ease and thickness in cutting which comes of the dew. So I at once began to sharpen my scythe.

There is an art also in the sharpening of a scythe, and it is worth describing carefully. Your blade must be dry, and that is why you will see men rubbing the scythe-blade with

3

grass before they whet it. Then also your rubber must be quite dry, and on this account it is a good thing to lay it on your coat and keep it there during all your day's mowing. The scythe you stand upright, with the blade pointing away from you, and you put your left hand firmly on the back of the blade, grasping it: then you pass the rubber first down one side of the blade-edge and then down the other, beginning near the handle and going on to the point and working quickly and hard. When you first do this you will, perhaps, cut your hand; but it is only at first that such an accident will happen to you.

To tell when the scythe is sharp enough this is the rule. First the stone clangs and grinds against the iron harshly; then it rings musically to one note; then, at last, it purrs as though the iron and stone were exactly suited. When you hear this, your scythe is sharp enough; and I, when I heard it that June dawn, with everything quite silent except the birds, let down the scythe and bent myself to mow.

When one does anything anew, after so many years, one fears very much for one's trick or habit. But all things once learnt are easily recoverable, and I very soon recovered the swing and power of the mower. Mowing well and mowing badly—or rather not mowing at all—are separated by very little; as is also true of writing verse, of playing the fiddle, and of dozens of other things, but of nothing more than of believing. For the bad or young or untaught mower without tradition, the mower Promethean, the mower original and contemptuous of the past, does all these things: He leaves great crescents of grass uncut. He digs the point of the scythe hard into the ground with a jerk. He loosens the handles and even the fastening of the blade. He twists the blade with his blunders, he blunts the blade, he chips it, dulls it, or breaks it clean off at the tip. If any one is standing by he cuts him in the ankle. He sweeps up into the air wildly, with nothing to resist his stroke. He drags up earth with the grass, which is like making the meadow

[THE MOWER: ABERGLASLYN

bleed. But the good mower who does things just as they
should be done and have been for a hundred thousand years,
falls into none of these fooleries. He goes forward very
steadily, his scythe-blade just barely missing the ground,
every grass falling; the swish and rhythm of his mowing are
always the same.

So great an art can only be learnt by continual practice;
but this much is worth writing down, that, as in all good
work, to know the thing with which you work is the core
of the affair. Good verse is best written on good paper
with an easy pen, not with a lump of coal on a whitewashed
wall. The pen thinks for you; and so does the scythe mow
for you if you treat it honourably and in a manner that
makes it recognize its service. The manner is this. You
must regard the scythe as a pendulum that swings, not as a
knife that cuts. A good mower puts no more strength into
his stroke than into his lifting. Again, stand up to your
work. The bad mower, eager and full of pain, leans forward
and tries to force the scythe through the grass. The good
mower, serene and able, stands as nearly straight as the
shape of the scythe will let him, and follows up every stroke
closely, moving his left foot forward. Then also let every
stroke get well away. Mowing is a thing of ample gestures,
like drawing a cartoon. Then, again, get yourself into a
mechanical and repetitive mood: be thinking of anything
at all but your mowing, and be anxious only when there
seems some interruption to the monotony of the sound. In
this mowing should be like one's prayers—all of a sort and
always the same, and so made that you can establish a
monotony and work them, as it were, with half your mind:
that happier half, the half that does not bother.

In this way, when I had recovered the art after so many
years, I went forward over the field, cutting lane after lane
through the grass, and bringing out its most secret essences
with the sweep of the scythe until the air was full of odours.
At the end of every lane I sharpened my scythe and looked

back at the work done, and then carried my scythe down again upon my shoulder to begin another. So, long before the bell rang in the chapel above me—that is, long before six o'clock, which is the time for the *Angelus*—I had many swathes already lying in order parallel like soldiery; and the high grass yet standing, making a great contrast with the shaven part, looked dense and high.

HILAIRE BELLOC, *Hills and the Sea.*

## The Spacious Days

AND so it went on, year after year, one continual hopeless striving to feed the flock. Sheep! Sheep! It was always the sheep. Your life was ruled by them, the whole farm revolved round them, and in my case, my father's temper varied with the state of the flock's well-being. They were a kind of Moloch, to which we were all sacrificed.

The old labourer was quite right in saying that all we did was to wait upon their needs. He used to vent his hatred on them, when they were dipped. He would stand at the side of the swimming bath filled with Cooper's Dip, armed with a long pole with a cross-piece at the end, and push them under the evil-smelling liquid with great glee.

We got a little respite from this eternal striving to satisfy the sheep in August and September, when the whole farm concentrated on the harvest. Sometimes even the shepherd would help in the evenings in a condescending sort of way, as one conferring a favour. I generally used to take my dinner with me during harvest. Field work started at 6 a.m. and continued till 8 p.m., and it was much nicer to eat bread and cheese and cold bread pudding in the field, than to waste the dinner hour in the journey home and back.

Many people think that the agricultural labourer of those

days was slow in his movements. This is incorrect. He looked slow, I grant you, but the experience of countless ages had discovered the simplest and easiest way of doing his manifold laborious tasks, and years of practice had transformed his gnarled and clumsy hands into extraordinarily deft and dexterous instruments. Also, he struck a gait at any job which he could keep up from daylight to dark, day after day. Any attempt to hurry him was disastrous. He considered it to be a slight on him, and that you didn't realize that he always gave of his best.

When we were carrying corn the number of pitchers in the field loading the wagons, and the number of men at the rick emptying them, had to be regulated to a nicety to keep the wagons going backwards and forwards steadily without a hitch. That is where Tommy and the trap came in. Tommy would be required earlier during the harvest; as a matter of fact he stayed harnessed to the trap all day until knock-off time. The wagons were led from the field to the rick and back by small boys. One of my father's dictums was that two boys together did half as much as one boy by himself, and that three boys did nothing at all. Let two of the boys stop for a minute or two as they passed, one with a full wagon and the other with an empty one, and the whole business of carrying was disorganized. Then, from some point of vantage, Tommy and the trap descended on them like the wrath of God. On these urgent occasions Thomas moved quite smartly.

I can appreciate now that my father's work in this way was very important. He would also play off the rick staff against the field men. Perhaps we would be a pitcher short of the required number owing to one of the carters having gone to the station for a load of something. Father would drive out to the other pitchers, and say to the head carter: ''Fraid you won't be able to keep us going so well to-day till Fred gets back. Still, we must put up with it. Just do the best you can.' Or perhaps the rick staff would be a man or two short for a similar reason, and it would be: 'I wonder if I'd better drive down to the dairy, and see if a milker can be spared for a bit. You chaps won't keep those pitchers going else.' 'Doan't 'ee worry, zur,' they would be sure to say, 'we'll manage somehow.'

If the occasion were desperate, and another hand must be got somehow, the shepherd was the last resort. You didn't send the foreman to see if the shepherd could get away for an hour or two. That would have been to court disaster. The sheep would have been in such a critical state that if the shepherd left for a moment they would all be sure to die. Neither was I sent. Youth hadn't the tact required for such a ticklish operation. Oh no! That was a job for the Guvnor, and we would see from the rick, Tommy being urged to his most furious speed up the far slope towards the sheepfold. Having arrived my father talked sheep, sheep, and nothing but sheep, thus relegating the harvest to an unimportant detail unworthy of mention. After a bit the shepherd would be sure to say: 'And how be getten on wi' the carrying, zur?' 'Pretty fair, shepherd. We're a bit short-handed to-day. I'm on my way down to the village to see if I can pick up another man.' 'Well, zur, I be about straight yer just now, in a manner o' speaking. Ud it be any good if I were to gie 'ee a hand fer an hour or two?' And back to the harvest field would come Tommy, hauling both the shepherd and my father, who had achieved his object without mentioning it. All this may sound childish to many people, but some will, I hope, recognize it for what it undoubtedly was—pure genius.

A. G. STREET, *Farmer's Glory*.

# Downland Sheep

HOUGH I have now travelled the Sussex-downs upwards of irty years, yet I still investigate that chain of majestic ountains with fresh admiration year by year; and think see new beauties every time I traverse it. This range, hich runs from Chichester eastward as far as East-Bourn, about sixty miles in length, and is called The South Downs, roperly speaking, only round Lewes. As you pass along ou command a noble view of the wild, or weald, on one and, and the broad downs and sea on the other. Mr Ray sed to visit a family [1] just at the foot of these hills, and was ravished with the prospect from Plumpton-plain near ewes, that he mentions those scapes in his *Wisdom of God the Works of the Creation* with the utmost satisfaction, and inks them equal to anything he had seen in the finest parts Europe.

For my own part, I think there is somewhat peculiarly veet and amusing in the shapely figured aspect of chalk-ills in preference to those of stone, which are rugged, roken, abrupt, and shapeless.

One thing is very remarkable as to the sheep: from the estward till you get to the river Adur all the flocks have orns, and smooth white faces, and white legs; and a horn-ss sheep is rarely to be seen: but as soon as you pass that ver eastward, and mount Beeding-hill, all the flocks at ace become hornless, or, as they call them, poll-sheep; and ave moreover black faces with a white tuft of wool on their reheads, and speckled and spotted legs: so that you would ink that the flocks of Laban were pasturing on one side of e stream, and the variegated breed of his son-in-law Jacob ere cantoned along on the other. And this diversity holds

[1] Mr Courthope, of Danny.

good respectively on each side from the valley of Bramb
and Beeding to the eastward, and westward all the who
length of the downs.   If you talk with the shepherds c
this subject, they tell you that the case has been so fro
time immemorial: and smile at your simplicity if you as
them whether the situation of these two different bree
might not be reversed?   However, an intelligent friend
mine near Chichester is determined to try the experimen
and has this autumn, at the hazard of being laughed a
introduced a parcel of black-faced hornless rams among h
horned western ewes.   The black-faced poll-sheep have tl
shortest legs and the finest wool.

GILBERT WHITE, *Natural History of Selborne.*

# Draught Oxen

THREE miles short of Braintree is Gosfield, well noted f
the seat of Lord Clare, and a fine park: but I take tl
opportunity of mentioning him here, chiefly on account of
stroke in agriculture, most unusual in Essex; which is tl
using oxen instead of horses, for all the purposes of draugh
His lordship, some years ago, keeping a farm in his hanc
and making many improvements in his park, introduced tl
practice from Gloucestershire, by purchasing a team of oxe
with all their geers, and hiring a driver in that country f
the instruction of his own people; at the same time he too
a plan of a very complete ox-house, with sundry adjoini:
conveniences, which he erected at Gosfield.

This scheme you may be very sure was highly ridicul
by all the neighbouring farmers, who would as soon belie
that an ox could speak as draw; but experience and ocul
demonstration convinced them of the contrary; and in o
instance remarkably, for a wagon with horses being set

village, and the ox-team passing by accidentally, the horses were taken off, after much rallying, and the oxen put to; who, to the amazement of the beholders, drew it out in triumph.

His lordship used them for the culture of his farm, as long as he kept it in his hands; and had once near thirty in constant work: he has ever since done all his business with them; such as carting in his park and plantations, carrying timber, and bringing coals, etc., from Colchester for his family. By very exact comparisons between the expenses of his oxen and the horses which he formerly kept for the same purposes, he clearly found there was a vast saving by using the first. Their food has constantly been hay in winter, and good grass in summer, without any oats. But notwithstanding the clear superiority, none of the farmers have followed the example, although a number of boys in the parish, and many labourers have gained a full knowledge of their management, and are as expert in driving them and breaking young beasts to the yoke, as any of their men can be with their horses.

You will excuse my being thus particular, in my account of this introduction of oxen into Essex; but the novelty of the thing in that county (his lordship's being the only team in it), the ridicule cast on it by the farmers, and the uninterrupted success it met with, has induced me to be more minute than otherwise I should have been.

ARTHUR YOUNG, *A Six Weeks Tour through the Southern Counties of England and Wales.*

# The Old Labourer

HE spoke of the cruelty of 'hittin' of 'em about over t[
head. The poor things never knows when they be rig[
after that. An' you can always tell, if they bin hit over t[
head: they won't let ye come near 'em. Well, it stands
reason—if you goes to touch their head they thinks you [
gwine to hit 'em. . . . There—it *is* a cruel thing to do.
I 'ad horses I 'd give a man the sack at a minute's notice,
I found 'n hittin' of 'em 'bout the head. Old Crosby, whe
I was workin' for he—I was gwine out wi' one of he 's hors
once, an' he says to me, "cut he's back-bone in two if [
likes," he says, "but don't hit 'n over the head." "N
sir," I says, "you may be very sure I shan't do that.
wouldn't do that. . . ." Now Doctor Fraser, when he use
to ride 'orseback, he used to knock he 's horse about sham
ful. Testy he is, you know; an' he 'd git in a temper a[
thresh the poor thing between the ears. There—I see
once, down there by Currie's, in Moorways Bottom by t[
brick-kiln there. The 'orse swerved across the road, an' [
began hittin' of 'n over the 'ead, an' he sittin' on 'n too. [
did. Even when he was on 'n, he threshed 'n between t[
ears. *Shame*ful! A feller at work there he says: "Pity
he don't throw th' old beggar off and roll over 'n in t[
ditch." And 't 'd ha' served 'n right if he had.

Bettesworth looked at it for half a minute; then: 'I r[
members one time when I was helpin' Beagley at a job ov[
there at ol' Miss Lawrence's at Cashford. There was a[
bricks, you know, right along by the ground for ventilati[
the floors. The bees had found this out, an' made a ne[
right in under her parlour floor, an' they used to come u[
through somewhere. At last she sent out to Beagley-

the place was reg'lar swarmin' wi' bees," she said, "so 's
he cou'n't bide there." Well, I laughed an' I gits a long
tick an' I pokes it into one o' these here holes. *Out* they
ll come—oh, ther' must ha' bin *thousands* and *thou*sands of
em—an' then I *did* laugh. We all got out o' the way 's
ast as we could. Miss Lawrence run, and the servant she
un, an' so did the man what was there. He was lame, an'
e went hoppin' off . . . !'

'But didn't they sting you?'

'Oh, they come for us, and we kep' brushin' of em off out
f our hair. But they whipped into us. The chap 'long o'
e, he was stung; but they never touched Beagley once.'

'How did you get on?'

'Oh, I was had in five or six places: but Beagley he on'y
ughed an' said: "That jest serves you right for makin' a
ame of 'em." They never touched he. And he went in-
oors an' fetched up the floor, an' chucked all the stuff out
—sand and bees and all—with his hands. There *is* some
ke that, as bees won't touch; and others, ye see, they don't
are go near where they be.'

'I 'm not fond of 'em, myself.'

'Oh, I don't mind 'em. That time as I hived some, they
ever hurt me. Still, *some* they 'd set on to. They be little
ings; an' yet ye see they can knock ye back'ards.'

And in the evening, when the day's picking is done, comes
e heaviest part of their work for Bettesworth and his
llow pole-pullers. Like a wise and careful farmer (Bettes-
orth admires the care which he suffers for) the master will
ve no horses trampling over his hop-ground. All the
wly-picked hops, emptied out from the baskets into coarse
en bags or 'sarpliers,' must be carried out of the ground
the waiting wagon. Some fifteen or sixteen bushels these
rpliers hold; and now that the hops are so wet the load is
heavy one—a hundredweight and a half in every one,
ttesworth reckons roughly, adding that 'it takes two men

to lift a bag up on to yer back.' And in this season from t
clammy load the water squeezes out and down the bearer
back 'a pailful at a time.' This across sticky clay, t
feet slipping at every step. Finally there are the two mil
to walk, and by the time that home is reached, it is da
again.

From dark to dark—say fifteen hours of it—is Bette
worth's average of work now. He came to see me th
evening. Hearing by his voice that he was tired, I broug
him in to have some beer; and while he drank it I notic
how rough and battered was his appearance. The old brov
cheeks were scratched by the hop-bines; they were hot ai
burnt with the beating of the wind and rain into eve
scratch. Mine, probably, was not the first beer he had ha
but in front of it there had been prolonged toil, and now t
old man was a picture of bedraggled weariness. In talkii
his head twitched over sideways, drowsily his eyes blinke
and his speech came slow and as if thickened with sleepine
Doubtless the beer had not helped to clear it; but beer
none, it was the usual straightforward practical sense th
he talked, animated by good-temper and vivid interest
his subject. After fifteen hours, too, to be sitting down w
in itself a boon. He sat long, telling so much that the mc
of it must be briefly summarized, not reported. . . .

'It *have* give it to my leg where I broke 'n. I got
bandaged up since Sunday. I pulled the bandages as tig
as ever I could pull 'em—but it have give me something. .
Ye see 't en't like level sailin'. The mud clogs under yo
shoes in lumps and twistës yer feet over. And where
be now, we got to carry the bags right out over two acres
'taters. Las' night the 'tater haulm—'twas up above c
knees, an' we was reg'lar wet through with it. 'T have be
dry to-day, but sweat . . . ! There, my leg an' stockin' w
reg'lar soppin' wet where I 've sweat wi' the pain, fro
carryin'. Still, I stuck to 't. There was fifty bags to-nig
an' we had to carry 'em right past sixty hills o' hops (ab

ιundred and twenty yards) an' then across these two acres
'taters where the ground was all ridged up.  Nine bags
me to my share—'cause we takes 'em turn an' turn about;
d I didn't hardly know how to keep going.  I was purty
ar ready to fall down when I come to the wagon—but
ll, when I 'd carried one there was nothin' for 't but to go
ck an' git another.  But my mate, he knowed how my
ς was, an' so when I come for my last bag he says, "Now
ok 'ere," he says, "if I sees you go to lift that up on your
ck, I shall knock 'n off again."  "If you do," I says, "I
all knock ye down."  And so I should.  "Well but," he
ys, "you may jest as well let me carry 'n, and you can be
ewerin' up this 'n for me."  "No," I says, "it 's my turn
d I en't gwine to flinch."  "I knows you don't want to
nch," he says, "but I don't mind doin' of it for *you*."  And
e foreman standin' there says: "No, old Fred 've worked
·le-pullin' 'long o' me thirty year, and I never knowed 'n
nch yet."  "No," I says, "and I ben't gwine to now." . . .
ιt never no more, not another year . . . not if I en't got
·thin' better 'n taters to live off from. . . .'
So the old man gained his point, too proud to succumb to
y weakness; yet well aware how next year may prove his
·le-pulling days to be over for ever.

GEORGE BOURNE, *The Bettesworth Book.*

# The Winnowers

BETWIXT two billows of the downs
 The little hamlet lies,
And nothing sees but the bald crowns
 Of the hills, and the blue skies.

Clustering beneath the long descent
 And grey slopes of the wold,

The red roofs nestle, oversprent
  With lichen yellow as gold.

We found it in the midday sun
  Basking, what time of year
The thrush his singing has begun,
  Ere the first leaves appear.

High from his load a woodman pitched
  His faggots on the stack:
Knee-deep in straw the cattle twitched
  Sweet hay from crib and rack:

And from the barn hard by was borne
  A steady muffled din,
By which we knew that threshèd corn
  Was winnowing, and went in.

The sunbeams on the motey air
  Streamed through the open door,
And on the brown arms moving bare,
  And the grain upon the floor.

One turns the crank, one stoops to feed
  The hopper, lest it lack,
One in the bushel scoops the seed,
  One stands to hold the sack.

We watched the good grain rattle down,
  And the awns fly in the draught;
To see us both so pensive grown
  The honest labourers laughed:

Merry they were, because the wheat
  Was clean and plump and good,
Pleasant to hand and eye, and meet
  For market and for food.

It chanced we from the city were,
    And had not got us free
In spirit from the store and stir
    Of its immensity:

But here we found ourselves again.
    Where humble harvests bring
After much toil but little grain,
    'Tis merry winnowing.

            ROBERT BRIDGES, *Shorter Poems.*

# The Ploughing Lesson

THE plough was back at the end of its journey, and Kindred, as he took more stubble into his compass, drew up on the headland to the spot where he intended to start his new furrow, stopping just level with Everard to give his team a breather. They had met before once or twice at 'The Olive Leaf,' but Kindred, though not uncompanionable, was a shy man of few words, and they did not know each other well.

He was square-shouldered, of middle height; his long face, ruddy and straight-nosed, was made even longer by a straggly fair beard, greying now—he was verging on sixty—but there was a quick, live gleam in his pale-blue eye. His ancient, ribbonless hat, his baggy coat, and close-fitting corduroy breeches had been faded by sun and rain to a harmonious pattern of nondescript colour, which gave them almost a timeless aspect, as if they might have grown out of the soil on which he worked. He raised a finger to Everard, who returned the greeting.

'You're making a wholly good job of that fence,' he said. 'I remember that was seven years ago when Henry last backheaded that; I had a crop of peas here then. I may

c

get a crop off my hidland now that 's cut agin; that kee
the sun off something terrible. You 've cut that wholl
tidy too.'

'I 'm glad you think so,' said Everard, gratified at th
compliment. 'It 's pretty tough work, but it doesn't lool
so tough as your ploughing.'

Kindred paused to light his pipe.

'Oh, I don't know,' he said, after a few puffs. 'That ain'
so bad as it fare to you. That 's on a slope, you see, and th
horses make you hurry, but that don't plough so bad. That '
be a real nice piece of land if only I could drain it. Come
wet time that 's wonderful mushy. We have to plough i
on the stetch, but there, I doubt you 'on't know what tha
mean as you ain't done no ploughing.'

'No, I haven't,' said Everard, 'though I know what th
stetch-work is. But I was just thinking how I 'd like t
be able to; and that field of yours is a picture.'

'Yes,' said Kindred, 'I do like the look of a bit of fresl
plough. I can't deny it. But do you step over the hedg
and try a furrow to see how you like it.'

Everard hesitated. 'I shouldn't like to spoil the look c
your field,' he said.

'Oh, that don't matter,' Kindred reassured him. ''Tain'
as if that was on the road for folks to see; and you 'on't d
all that harm.'

--'All right, then, I will,' said Everard, pushing his wa
through a thin spot in the hedge and leaping the ditch
'But you 'll have to tell me how to set about it.'

'I 'll do that, all right,' said Kindred, who had faced hi
horses up the field again. 'Now get you hold of the handles
What you 've got to do is watch the coulter, that ther
knife in front that cut into the weeds—you can't see th
share, 'cause that 's underground; and you 've got to kee
that coulter allus the same distance from the edge of you
last furrow—you can see the line it make; so, when you wan
your coulter, and becourse, your share underneath, to go t

the right, you bring down your left handle, and when you want it to go to the left, you bring down your right. Got that?'

'I think so,' said Everard, desperately trying to repeat the instructions in his own head.

'Well, now, to enter your share, lift up your handles just a bit, and tell 'em to goo on. No, no, don't touch the line. Dolly 'll do all the guiding. She can't go wrong 'cause she 's a-walking in my last furrow. Now then, up with them handles. Dolly! Short! Goo on!' He uttered these last commands in a curious complaining tone from the back of his throat, a little like the mooing of a cow.

There was a rattle of chain harness, the whipple-trees lifted, the horses strained. There was a tiny pause while the uptilted share burrowed its nose in the stubble, and then with a soft slither it plunged underground, as the horses dropped into their stride.

'Down with them handles!' cried Kindred.

Everard obeyed, and suddenly found himself pulled away after the horses, his feet in the soft yielding furrow striving desperately to keep up with his hands, which with equal desperation strove to hold the swaying handles level. His eye was fixed upon the coulter blade in front of him, and the thin wriggling line that it traced in the brown earth; he had no time to look at anything else. Kindred's voice admonishing the team seemed to come out of the far distance. How that line wriggled, it would get away to the right, towards the edge of the next furrow; he could not stop it, it veered nearer and nearer.

'Hey!' cried Kindred, 'look what you 're doing! You 'll be out of your furrow.'

Everard groped in his mind for the remedy; it was something to do with the handles, he must veer to the left. He put his weight on the left handle. The next moment the plough was out of the ground, jolting and tearing in the bottom of the adjacent furrow.

'Woa, woa!' shouted Kindred.

The horses stopped obediently.

'No, you should have pressed the other way,' he cried. 'Right handle take you left, left take you right.'

'Like a boat's rudder,' thought Everard. 'Sorry,' he said, 'I forgot.'

'Oh, don't you worry,' replied Kindred, laughing, 'that 'on't do no harm. Only that 's the worst thing to put right, 'cause you 've got to hup-back to where you came out of the furrow, and you 've got to drag the plough yourself 'cause the horses can't push with chains. Come on now. Hup-back, hup-back!' he called to the horses.

They backed reluctantly and awkwardly as horses always do.

'Pull now, man,' said Kindred, 'back with her!'

Everard tugged at the handles with all his weight and brought it jerk by jerk to the spot where he had broken his furrow.

'That 's heavy,' he puffed. 'I 'm glad I don't have to pull the plough.'

'No,' laughed Kindred, 'you don't want to leave your furrow too often, do you? Now, do you remember about them handles this time.'

The share was entered again, Kindred shouted to the horses, and Everard was off again on what seemed to him like a steeplechase for the opposite hedge. He mastered the handles this time; it was wonderful how the coulter answered to them, and he made his furrow describe a good deal more curves than was needful, displaying his skill.

'That ain't a see-saw,' growled Kindred beside him. 'Watch the coulter.'

Everard curbed his enthusiasm and the furrow straightened.

H. W. FREEMAN, Down in the Valley.

# In Time of 'The Breaking of Nations'

ONLY a man harrowing clods
  In a slow silent walk
With an old horse that stumbles and nods
  Half asleep as they stalk.

Only thin smoke without flame
  From the heaps of couch-grass;
Yet this will go onward the same
  Though Dynasties pass.

Yonder a maid and her wight
  Come whispering by;
War's annals will cloud into night
  Ere their story die.

THOMAS HARDY, *Collected Poems*.

# 2. Nature

# A Cold Day at Silchester

A FEW more steps and I came upon as pretty a little scene in bird life as one could wish for: twenty to twenty-five small birds of different species—tits, wrens, dunnocks, thrushes, blackbirds, chaffinches, yellowhammers—were congregated on the lower outside twigs of a bramble bush and on the bare ground beside it close to the foot of the wall. The sun shone full on that spot, and they had met for warmth and for company. The tits and wrens were moving quietly about in the bush; others were sitting idly or pruning their feathers on the twigs or the ground. Most of them were making some kind of small sound—little exclamatory chirps, and a variety of chirrupings, producing the effect of a pleasant conversation going on among them. This was suddenly suspended on my appearance, but the alarm was soon over, and, seeing me seated on a fallen stone and motionless, they took no further notice of me. Two blackbirds were there, sitting a little way apart on the bare ground; these were silent, the raggedest, rustiest-looking members of that little company; for they were moulting, and their drooping wings and tails had many unsightly gaps in them where the old feathers had dropped out before the new ones had grown. They were suffering from that annual sickness with temporary loss of their brightest faculties which all birds experience in some degree; the unseasonable rains and cold winds had been bad for them, and now they were having their sun-bath, their best medicine and cure.

By and by a pert-looking, bright-feathered, dapper cock chaffinch dropped down from the bush, and, advancing to one of the two, the rustiest and most forlorn-looking, started running round and round him as if to make a close inspection of his figure, then began to tease him. At first I thought it was all in fun—merely animal spirit which in birds often discharges itself in this way in little pretended attacks and fights. But the blackbird had no play and no fight in him, no heart to defend himself; all he did was to try to avoid the strokes aimed at him, and he could not always escape them. His spiritlessness served to inspire the chaffinch with greater boldness, and then it appeared that the gay little creature was really and truly incensed, possibly because the rusty, draggled, and listless appearance of the larger bird was offensive to him. Anyhow, the persecutions continued, increasing in fury until they could not be borne, and the blackbird tried to escape by hiding in the bramble. But he was not permitted to rest there; out he was soon driven and away into another bush, and again into still another farther away, and finally he was hunted over the sheltering wall into the bleak wind on the other side. Then the persecutor came back and settled himself on his old perch on the bramble, well satisfied at his victory over a bird so much bigger than himself. All was again peace and harmony in the little social gathering, and the pleasant talkee-talkee went on as before. About five minutes passed, then the hunted blackbird returned, and, going to the identical spot from which he had been driven, composed himself to rest; only now he sat facing his lively little enemy.

I was astonished to see him back; so, apparently, was the chaffinch. He started, craned his neck, and regarded his adversary first with one eye then with the other. 'What, rags and tatters, back again so soon!' I seemed to hear him say. 'You miserable travesty of a bird, scarcely fit for a weasel to dine on! Your presence is an insult to us, but I 'll soon settle you. You 'll feel the cold on the other side of the wall when I 've knocked off a few more of your rusty rags.'

Down from his perch he came, but no sooner had he touched his feet to the ground than the blackbird went straight at him with extraordinary fury. The chaffinch, taken by surprise, was buffeted and knocked over, then, recovering himself, fled in consternation, hotly pursued by the sick one. Into the bush they went, but in a moment they were out again, darting this way and that, now high up in the trees, now down to the ground, the blackbird always close behind; and no little bird flying from a hawk could have exhibited a greater terror than that pert chaffinch—that vivacious and most pugnacious little cock bantam. At last they went quite away, and were lost to sight. By and by the blackbird returned alone, and, going once more to his place near the second bird, he settled down comfortably to finish his sun-bath in peace and quiet.

I had assuredly witnessed a new thing on that unpromising day, something quite different from anything witnessed in my wide rambles; and, though a little thing, it had been a most entertaining comedy in bird life with a very proper ending. It was clear that the sick blackbird had bitterly resented the treatment he had received; that, brooding on it out in the cold, his anger had made him strong, and that he came back determined to fight, with his plan of action matured. He was not going to be made a fool of every time!

W. H. Hudson, *Afoot in England*.

# A Trapped Eagle

I cannot omit here a small adventure, which was very surprizing to me on this journey; passing this plain country, we came to an open peice of ground where a neighbouring gentleman had at a great expence laid out a proper peice of land for a Decoy, or Duck-coy, as some call it; the works were but newly done, the planting young, the ponds very large, and well made; but the proper places for shelter of the fowl not cover'd, the trees not being grown, and men were still at work improving, and enlarging, and planting on the adjoyning heath, or common: Near the decoy keeper's house, were some places where young decoy-ducks were hatch'd, or otherwise kept to fit them for their work; To preserve them from vermin, polecats, kites, and such like, they had set traps, as is usual in such cases, and a gibbet by it, where abundance of such creatures as were taken were hang'd up for show.

While the decoy man was busy showing the new-works, he was alarm'd with a great cry about this house for Help, Help, and away he run, like the wind, guessing, as we suppos'd, that something was catch'd in the trap.

It was a good big boy about 13 or 14 year old, that cry'd out, for coming to the place, he found a great fowl catch'd by the leg in the trap, which yet was so strong, and so outrageous, that the boy going too near him, he flew at him, and frighted him, bit him, and beat him with his wings, for he was too strong for the boy; as the master ran from the decoy, so another man-servant ran from the house, and finding a strange creature fast in the trap, not knowing what it was, laid at him with a great stick; the creature fought him a good while, but at length he struck him an unlucky blow, which quieted him; after this we all came up to see what was the matter, and found a monstrous eagle caught by the leg in the trap, and kill'd by the fellow's cudgel, as above.

When the master came to know what it was, and that his man had kill'd it, he was ready to kill the fellow for his pains, for it was a noble creature indeed, and would have been worth a great deal to the man to have it shown about the country, or to have sold to any gentleman curious in such things; but the eagle was dead, and there we left it: 'Tis probable this eagle had flown over the sea from France, either there, or at the Isle of Weight, where the Channel is not so wide; for we do not find that any eagles are known to breed in those parts of Britain.

DANIEL DEFOE, *A Tour Through England and Wales.*

# The White Owl

ᵛERY different was the life of the white owl in Chichester.
t the inn where I stayed on my last visit, I found three
nhappy prisoners; two of these, a jackdaw and a blackbird,
ere kept in rabbit-hutch-like cages fixed against the ceiling
f a long, narrow, dimly-lighted passage.  It was sad to see
he poor daw, the bird that loves soaring in wind and sun-
nine, shut up in that narrow house in a perpetual twilight,
is head, when he sat on his perch, pressed against the
eiling.  He always perched at the same end of his hutch,
nd the constant pressure of his head on one spot had made
 hole in the plaster above.  People were passing and re-
assing through that passage all day long, but without
oticing the daw; for he was hung above the line, so to say,
nd to see him it was necessary to look up.  Now, I observed
hat whenever I paused before the cage and looked up, the
ird would instantly jump on to his perch, and, turning his
ack to me, fix his head against the ceiling in the corner,
nd remain motionless in that strange position.  A silent,
ullen daw—and no wonder!  He did not, like Sterne's
aptive starling, cry continually, 'I can't get out'; he made
o cry, and had no hope of ever feeling the wind and the sun,
r ever seeing the blue sky and green earth again.  Eight
o nine years had he been immured in that cursed prison, and
e would never leave it until his tortured life had left him;
hen his dead body would be taken out, and another bird,
 dare say, put there in his place.

  The third prisoner was the owl, and I think he was even
vorse off than the others; for he was kept in an always
nalodorous and usually uncovered cage, in the kitchen,
vhere a big fire was burning sixteen to seventeen hours
very day.  The heat must have been—and alas! still must

T OCKLEY, SURREY]

be—dreadful to the poor bird; but if speech had been given
him he would, I think, have complained most of the ga
jets: they were burning all about him until twelve o'clock
every night, and the sensation they produced must hav
been as of fine heated needles, heated red and heated white
stabbing and pricking his sensitive eye-balls. In thi
chamber of torture the miserable bird had existed for nine
months.

When I went to the landlady to plead for the owl, I wa
very diplomatic, remembering what certain wise men have
taught us—namely, that if we want to get anything out o
anybody we must not begin by rubbing him up the wron
way. I praised her greatly for her merciful heart, and tol
her how it had delighted me to hear her fame in Chicheste
as a lover and protector of animals. But her treatment o
her feathered pets was wrong; and in mild language I im
parted my views on the subject. She was disturbed at wha
I said about the owl, and began to excuse herself, sayin
that she had taken in the bird solely to give it a safe an
happy home, but she had no desire to keep it as it was
silent dull bird, and that if I wished I could take it awa
and set it free.

I was delighted at my success, and promised to find befor
long a suitable home for the bird.

For some days after that I kept a look out during m
rambles; and one afternoon, in the maritime district, I cam
to a small village which struck me as an ideal home for a
owl. For it was a small and most rustic place, consistin
of a little church and a great thatched barn and many farr
buildings. But the farm-house itself, even in this land o
great old farms that were once manors, was a surprise t
me. It was a very large low stone building, partly ove
grown with ivy, and nearly surrounded by an ancient fos
with great old elm trees growing out of the banks. Th
people who lived in this grey old manse were worthy of the
home: the lady of the house, who received me, was youn

and fair to see, and gracious in mind and manner; and when I told her my errand, she said that she and her husband were very fond of birds and had a peculiar regard for the white owl; and that if I would take and release it in their barn she herself would place food for it there every day and see that it was not disturbed, until it had recovered its strength and the use of its wings and could find its own living.

Meanwhile my landlady had changed her mind, and when I was ready to take the bird she informed me that she had decided not to part with it; that on thinking the matter over she had found out that she had become attached to the owl, and she also thought that the bird would be unhappy if taken from the home and the surroundings he was accustomed to.

In vain I begged and pleaded, not that day only, but the next, and for several days. She would not part with the bird for love or money. Up till then I had visited the bird every day, and opening its cage would put my hand in to caress it. It liked to be gently stroked on the breast, and when caressed in this way would play with my fingers, biting them but very gently with his beak. But from that time I was ashamed to go near him, or even to look at him; for I had promised him his liberty, and could not keep my word. Nor was it necessary that I should look at to see him; his melancholy image was too deeply graved in my mind—a feathered Dreyfus, Semitic features and all, the head bowed, the weary eyes closed, the hooked nose just visible amidst a wilderness of white whiskers. I could only try to believe that there is some foundation for the ancient belief held in so many lands, that the owl is indeed a supernatural, or sacred, bird; that when this captive had been tortured to death and its carcass thrown into the dust-heap, the loving kindness that had been shown to him would have a swift and suitable reward.

W. H. HUDSON, *Nature in Downland.*

# The Lily-pool

WHAT sees our mailie [1] in the lily-pool,
  What sees she with that large surprise?
What sees our mailie in the lily-pool
  With all the violet of her big eyes—
    Our mailie in the lily-pool?

She sees herself within the lily-pool,
  Herself in flakes of brown and white—
Herself beneath the slab that is the lily-pool,
  The green and liquid slab of light
  With cups of silver dight,
  Stem-rooted in the depths of amber night
That hold the hollows of the lily-pool—
Our own dear lily-pool.

And does she gaze into the lily-pool
  As one that is enchanted?
Or does she try the cause to find
  How the reflection's slanted,
That sleeps within the lily-pool?
  Or does she take it all for granted,
With the sweet natural logic of her kind?
  The lazy logic of the lily-pool,
  Our own bright, innocent, stupid lily-pool!

She knows that it is nice—our lily-pool:
  She likes the water-rings around her knees;
  She likes the shadow of the trees,

---

[1] A cow without horns.

That droop above the lily-pool;
   She likes to scatter with a silly sneeze
The long-legged flies that skim the lily-pool—
The peaceful-sleeping, baby lily-pool.

   So may I look upon the lily-pool
   Nor ever in the slightest care
   Why I am there;
Why upon land and sea
Is ever stamped the inevitable me;
But rather say with that most gentle fool:—
'How pleasant is this lily-pool!
How nice and cool!
Be off, you long-legged flies! O, what a spree!
To drive the flies from off the lily-pool!
From off this most sufficient, absolute lily-pool!'

              T. E. BROWN, *Collected Poems*.

# On the River

'WHAT are you looking at?' said the Rat presently, when the edge of their hunger was somewhat dulled, and the Mole's eyes were able to wander off the table-cloth a little.

'I am looking,' said the Mole, 'at a streak of bubbles that I see travelling along the surface of the water. That is a thing that strikes me as funny.'

'Bubbles? Oho!' said the Rat, and chirrupped cheerily in an inviting sort of way.

A broad glistening muzzle showed itself above the edge of the bank, and the Otter hauled himself out and shook the water from his coat.

'Greedy beggars!' he observed, making for the provender. 'Why didn't you invite me, Ratty?'

D

'This was an impromptu affair,' explained the Rat. 'B
the way—my friend Mr Mole.'

'Proud, I 'm sure,' said the Otter, and the two animal
were friends forthwith.

'Such a rumpus everywhere!' continued the Otter. 'A
the world seems out on the river to-day. I came up thi
backwater to try and get a moment's peace, and then stumbl
upon you fellows!—At least—I beg pardon—I don't exactl
mean that, you know.'

There was a rustle behind them, proceeding from a hedg
wherein last year's leaves still clung thick, and a strip
head, with high shoulders behind it, peered forth on then

'Come on, old Badger!' shouted the Rat.

The Badger trotted forward a pace or two; then grunted
'H 'm! Company,' and turned his back and disappeare
from view.

'That 's *just* the sort of fellow he is!' observed the di
appointed Rat. 'Simply hates Society! Now we shan
see any more of him to-day. Well, tell us *who 's* out o
the river?'

'Toad 's out, for one,' replied the Otter. 'In his brand
new wager-boat; new togs, new everything!'

The two animals looked at each other and laughed.

'Once, it was nothing but sailing,' said the Rat. 'The
he tired of that and took to punting. Nothing would pleas
him but to punt all day and every day, and a nice mess
made of it. Last year it was house-boating, and we all ha
to go and stay with him in his house-boat, and pretend w
liked it. He was going to spend the rest of his life in
house-boat. It 's all the same, whatever he takes up;
gets tired of it, and starts on something fresh.'

'Such a good fellow, too,' remarked the Otter reflectivel
'But no stability—especially in a boat!'

From where they sat they could get a glimpse of the ma
stream across the island that separated them; and just th
a wager-boat flashed into view, the rower—a short, sto

gure—splashing badly and rolling a good deal, but working
is hardest. The Rat stood up and hailed him, but Toad
—for it was he—shook his head and settled sternly to
is work.

'He 'll be out of the boat in a minute if he rolls like that,'
aid the Rat, sitting down again.

'Of course he will,' chuckled the Otter. 'Did I ever tell
ou that good story about Toad and the lock-keeper? It
appened this way. Toad . . .'

An errant May-fly swerved unsteadily athwart the current
a the intoxicated fashion affected by young bloods of May-
ies seeing life. A swirl of water and a 'cloop!' and the
lay-fly was visible no more.

Neither was the Otter.

The Mole looked down. The voice was still in his ears,
ut the turf whereon he had sprawled was clearly vacant.
ot an Otter to be seen, as far as the distant horizon.

But again there was a streak of bubbles on the surface of
he river.

The Rat hummed a tune, and the Mole recollected that
nimal etiquette forbade any sort of comment on the sudden
isappearance of one's friends at any moment, for any
eason or no reason whatever.

'Well, well,' said the Rat, 'I suppose we ought to be
loving. I wonder which of us had better pack the luncheon-
asket?' He did not speak as if he was frightfully eager
or the treat.

'O, please let me,' said the Mole. So, of course, the Rat
t him.

Packing the basket was not quite such pleasant work as
npacking the basket. It never is. But the Mole was bent
a enjoying everything, and although just when he had got
ie basket packed and strapped up tightly he saw a plate
aring up at him from the grass, and when the job had been
one again the Rat pointed out a fork which anybody ought
⟩ have seen, and last of all, behold! the mustard pot, which

he had been sitting on without knowing it—still, somehow
the thing got finished at last, without much loss of temper

The afternoon sun was getting low as the Rat sculle
gently homewards in a dreamy mood, murmuring poetry
things over to himself, and not paying much attention t
Mole. But the Mole was very full of lunch, and self-satis
faction, and pride, and already quite at home in a boat (s
he thought) and was getting a bit restless besides: an
presently he said: 'Ratty! Please, I want to row, now!'

The Rat shook his head with a smile. 'Not yet, my youn
friend,' he said, 'wait till you 've had a few lessons. It
not so easy as it looks.'

The Mole was quiet for a minute or two. But he bega
to feel more and more jealous of the Rat, sculling so strongl
and so easily along, and his pride began to whisper that h
could do it every bit as well. He jumped up and seized th
sculls, so suddenly, that the Rat, who was gazing out ove
the water and saying more poetry-things to himself, wa
taken by surprise, and fell backwards off his seat with h
legs in the air for a second time, while the triumphant Mol
took his place and grabbed the sculls with entire confidenc

'Stop it, you *silly* ass!' cried the Rat, from the bottom o
the boat. 'You can't do it! You 'll have us over!'

The Mole flung his sculls back with a flourish, and made
great dig at the water. He missed the surface altogethe
his legs flew up above his head, and he found himself lyin
on the top of the prostrate Rat. Greatly alarmed, he mad
a grab at the side of the boat, and the next moment—
Sploosh!

Over went the boat, and he found himself struggling i
the river.

KENNETH GRAHAME, *The Wind in the Willows.*

## Winter : East Anglia

In a frosty sunset
  So fiery red with cold
The footballers' onset
  Rings out glad and bold;
Then boys from daily tether
  With famous dogs at heel
In starlight meet together
  And to farther hedges steal;
Where the rats are pattering
  In and out the stacks,
Owls with hatred chattering
  Swoop at the terriers' backs.
And, frost forgot, the chase grows hot
  Till a rat 's a foolish prize,
But the cornered weasel stands his ground,
Shrieks at the dogs and boys set round,
Shrieks as he knows they stand all round
  And hard as winter dies.

EDMUND BLUNDEN, *Poems 1914–30*.


## The Escape

DELIA licked her paw all night, only stopping to drink water
every now and again because she got so thirsty—for really,
inside, she was in every bit as much of a hurry as I was.
Now that she had seen Joan again she couldn't think of
anything else.

  'You 'd better take the first chance of escape that offers,'
she said, 'and I 'll follow when I can.'

[WOODLAND SNOW]

No sooner had I understood her to mean this than a loud grinding sound began outside. It was quite a familiar noise for it happened very often, but Delia was just as frightened every time as though she had never heard it before, and always set up the most dismal howl—as she did now. Then the front door was opened, and the horrible noise was so much louder that Delia rushed out of sight altogether. I didn't see where she went because I was peeping out of the door to catch sight of my enemy, the monkey, who always sat on the top of the noise. Old Mrs Bartram loved that monkey much better than she did me, and every time it came Sarah was sent out with a nut for it. I generally sat at the window and swore at it while this was going on, and it used to make awful grimaces at me in return.

But to-day I chanced to be in the hall, and there was the front door left open while Sarah was being fetched. It was too good a chance to miss. 'Wow-wow,' I screamed back into the house on a warning note to Delia to show I was doing something desperate, and out I rushed past the monkey, who screamed all manner of rudeness at me which I hadn't time to answer. I just went off full tilt in the direction which would lead home.

As ill-luck would have it the first thing I met was a dog, but I stood and faced it with yowls and growls till its owner arrived and put it on a lead. Then she said: 'Why, that's Miss Bartram's sweet little Siamese cat. It must have strayed. I must take it back.' And she held out her other hand, the one that wasn't holding the dog, to me, calling: 'Pussy, pussy—dear little pussy!'

I fled down the road, while her dog barked fit to choke itself, and some rude boys laughed. I came to a high hedge presently, and scrambled through it to find myself in somebody's garden. I waited there, well hidden in some bushes for a little while, and then came out very carefully and crossed the road to a field behind the opposite hedge. It was too dangerous to work my way along the main road by daylight. I must travel in the right direction as well as I could behind hedges and then come out in the dark, which never troubled me as it did dogs and human beings, and make up for lost time then.

But I saw it would take a long time to get home, and I hoped there would be a few mice and moles about for me to eat. Milk I shouldn't miss, and there was plenty of water in the ditches, I saw with satisfaction, for it had rained early that morning. As soon as it was dusk I came out boldly into the open and made off at a brisk pace in what I knew quite well was the right direction for the Manor House. And then a wonderful thing happened. I heard behind me something which made even me turn round with a loud cry of welcome.

It was pitter patter, pitter patter—but the one pitter patter in the world for me just then, which I should know anywhere, even though the familiar lilt of it was altered by a limp. Up trotted Delia, not a bit surprised this time, and licked my face.

'Oh, Delia, how did you find me?'

'You forget I'm a hound,' said Delia, 'and I'm every bit as proud of that as you are of being a Siamese. I can always find a living thing by its scent though I may not be so clever as you at finding a *place*.'

I rubbed against her legs and purred.

'I wish you wouldn't waste time so,' said Delia, 'your legs aren't nearly as long as mine, and we must get home to-night.'

'Oh, I can't!' I said in dismay, and began to run to keep up with Delia's trot. She *couldn't* go slowly if she tried. And now the tables were turned. It was the once timid Delia who took the lead. She was so fired by her love for Joan and the desire to get to her that nothing could keep her back, not even her poor paw, which was making her lame.

So away we went down the road together, and I dare say we looked very funny to human eyes, but there was nobody but walking, and when a car came we divided and dashed to opposite sides of the road. When the *real* dark came I took the lead again. I was so glad that my sight was better than Delia's, for then her long legs wouldn't tempt her to rush away to Joan without me—anyway, till daylight came. We travelled all that night, just stopping for an occasional pant or lick, or to drink any water that obligingly came our way. There came all too soon for me a fine, lovely morning; and now workmen on bicycles, maids on doorsteps, boys with milk carts, postmen with letters and, worst of all, dogs out for walks began to make their appearance.

'Let's get behind the hedges again,' I said.

'Why?' asked Delia. She thinks so slowly always.

'Because there's a large black dog coming up the hill,' I answered, the hair on my back already beginning to rise of itself.

'It's not as big as I am,' said Delia, 'I can protect you.' I hesitated, which was unlike me, and shows how you can be influenced by a friend's state of mind. In that second the dog saw me and made a rush. It was too late for the hedge, so I dashed up a lamp-post. But the lamp-post was made of some stuff much harder than wood, and didn't give me any hold for my claws. I yowled to Delia that any moment I should slip down into the jaws of the black fiend which stood waiting for me below. Delia was by nature very friendly, even with other dogs, and didn't like fighting a bit, but it was simply splendid to see her charge my enemy. He was very strong, but then, he hadn't Delia's size, and the fight was perfectly awful.

A crowd of shouting people collected from nowhere. A man with a stick tried to beat the dogs asunder, but they didn't seem to feel it. It was so exciting that I lost my balance and fell into the middle of it all, but the black dog didn't even see me. He was on his back and Delia had him by the throat. I got off to the hedge, darting between people's legs, and peeped through the bushes on the other side to see the end. Somebody dashed a pail of cold water over the scuffling pair, but they didn't feel that any more than the stick. Then somebody sprinkled something over them out of a pot, and this time Delia let go and sneezed and sneezed and sneezed and the enemy sneezed too.

And now someone came out of a house and dragged the black dog indoors, while Delia stood in the middle of the road—looking very wretched and with both her ears bleeding. A lady came out of another house with a bowl of water and began to bathe Delia's ears, and Delia didn't growl or bark at her at all, but licked the lady's hand as if she had known her always. Delia *would* do that, of course. . . .

I was so busy watching Delia that I forgot to attend to myself, and was wholly unprepared for the dreadful adventure that was approaching me.

A. M. M. HALES, *The Story of Ben-Ban.*

## Winter's Beauty

Is it not fine to walk in spring,
When leaves are born, and hear birds sing?
And when they lose their singing powers,
In summer, watch the bees at flowers?
Is it not fine, when summer's past,
To have the leaves, no longer fast,
Biting my heel where'er I go,
Or dancing lightly on my toe?
Now winter's here and rivers freeze;
As I walk out I see the trees,
Wherein the pretty squirrels sleep,
All standing in the snow so deep:
And every twig, however small,
Is blossomed white and beautiful.
Then welcome, winter, with thy power

To make this tree a big white flower;
To make this tree a lovely sight,
With fifty brown arms draped in white,
While thousands of small fingers show
In soft white gloves of purest snow.

W. H. DAVIES, *Collected Poems*.

# The Greenwood Tree

UNDER the greenwood tree
Who loves to lie with me,
And turn his merry note
Unto the sweet bird's throat,
Come hither, come hither, come hither:
Here shall he see
No enemy
But winter and rough weather.
Who doth ambition shun,
And loves to live i' the sun,
Seeking the food he eats,
And pleased with what he gets,
Come hither, come hither, come hither,
Here shall he see
No enemy
But winter and rough weather.

WILLIAM SHAKESPEARE, *As You Like It*.

# The Brook

WHEN he woke next morning, Bevis quite forgot what the Squirrel had told him; he jumped out of bed without thinking, and his right foot touched the floor first, and led him to the window. From the window he saw the Brook, and recollected that the Brook had promised to tell him what he was singing, so as soon as ever he could get out of doors away he went through the gateway the Grasshopper had shown him, and down to the hatch. Instead of coming quietly on tip-toe, as the Brook had told him, he danced up, and the Kingfisher heard him, and went off as before, whistling 'weep, weep.' Bevis stood on the brink and said: 'Brook, Brook, what are you singing? You promised to tell me what you were saying.'

The Brook did not answer, but went on singing. Bevis listened a minute, and then he picked up a willow leaf and threw it into the bubbles, and watched it go whirling round and round in the eddies, and back up under the fall, where it dived down, and presently came up again, and the stream took it and carried it away past the flags. 'Brook, Brook,' said Bevis, stamping his foot, 'tell me what you are singing.'

And the Brook, having now finished that part of his song, said: 'Bevis dear, sit down in the shadow of the willow, for it is very hot to-day, and the reapers are at work; sit down under the willow, and I will tell you as much as I can remember.'

'But the Reed said you could not remember anything,' said Bevis, leaning back against the willow.

'The Reed did not tell you the truth, dear; indeed, he does not know all; the fact is, the reeds are so fond of talking that I scarcely ever answer them now, or they would keep on all day long, and I should never hear the sound of my own voice,

which I like best. So I do not encourage them, and that i
why the reeds think I do not recollect.'

'And what is it that you sing about?' said Bevis, im
patiently.

'My darling,' said the Brook, 'I do not know myself alway
what I am singing about. I am so happy I sing, sing, an
never think about what it means; it does not matter wha
you mean as long as you sing. Sometimes I sing about th
sun, who loves me dearly, and tries all day to get at m
through the leaves and the green flags that hide me; h
sparkles on me everywhere he can, and does not like m
to be in the shadow. Sometimes I sing to the wind, wh
loves me next most dearly, and will come to me everywhere
in places where the sun cannot get. He plays with me when
ever he can, and strokes me softly, and tells me the thing
he has heard in the woods and on the hills, and sends dow
the leaves to float along, for he knows I like something t
carry. Fling me in some leaves, Bevis, dear.

'Sometimes I sing to the earth and the grass; they ar
fond of me, too, and listen the best of all. I sing loudest a
night, to the stars, for they are so far away they would no
otherwise hear me.'

'But what do you say?' said Bevis; but the Brook wa
too occupied now to heed him, and went on.

'Sometimes I sing to the trees; they, too, are fond of me
and come as near as they can; they would all come dow
close to me if they could. They love me like the rest
because I am so happy, and never cease my chaunting. I
I am broken to pieces against a stone, I do not mind in th
least; I laugh just the same, and even louder. When I com
over the hatch, I dash myself to fragments; and sometime
a rainbow comes and stays a little while with me. Th
trees drink me, and the grass drinks me, the birds come dow
and drink me; they splash me and are happy. The fishe
swim about, and some of them hide in deep corners. Roun
the bend I go, and the osiers say they never have enough o

[PRIMROSE

e. The long grass waves and welcomes me; the moorhens
oat with me; the Kingfisher is always with me somewhere,
nd sits on the bough to see his ruddy breast in the water.
nd you come, too, Bevis, now and then to listen to me;
nd it is all because I am so happy.'

'Why are you so happy?' said Bevis.

'I do not know,' said the Brook. 'Perhaps it is because
ll I think of is this minute; I do not know anything about
he minute just gone by, and I do not care one bit about
he minute that is just coming; all I care about is this minute,
his very minute now. Fling me in some more leaves, Bevis.
Why do you go about asking questions, dear? Why don't
ou sing, and do nothing else?'

RICHARD JEFFERIES, *Wood Magic*.

## From L'Allegro

HASTE thee, Nymph, and bring with thee
Jest, and youthful Jollity,
Quips and cranks and wanton wiles,
Nods and becks and wreathèd smiles,
Such as hang on Hebe's cheek,
And love to live in dimple sleek;
Sport that wrinkled Care derides,
And Laughter holding both his sides.
Come, and trip it, as you go,
On the light fantastic toe;
And in thy right hand lead with thee
The mountain-nymph, sweet Liberty;
And, if I give thee honour due,
Mirth, admit me of thy crew,
To live with her, and live with thee,
In unreprovèd pleasures free;

To hear the lark begin his flight,
And, singing, startle the dull night,
From his watch-tower in the skies,
Till the dappled dawn doth rise;
Then to come, in spite of sorrow,
And at my window bid good-morrow,
Through the sweet-briar or the vine,
Or the twisted eglantine;
While the cock, with lively din,
Scatters the rear of darkness thin;
And to the stack, or the barn-door,
Stoutly struts his dames before:
Oft listening how the hounds and horn
Cheerly rouse the slumbering morn,
From the side of some hoar hill,
Through the high wood echoing shrill:
Sometime walking, not unseen,
By hedgerow elms, on hillocks green,
Right against the eastern gate
Where the great Sun begins his state,
Robed in flames and amber light,
The clouds in thousand liveries dight;
While the ploughman, near at hand,
Whistles o'er the furrowed land,
And the milkmaid singeth blithe,
And the mower whets his scythe,
And every shepherd tells his tale
Under the hawthorn in the dale.

JOHN MILTON.

# 3. Trees

# Planting a Spinney

was told the other day a pleasant fact about Sir Henry
Campbell-Bannerman which will endear him still more to
some and make him appear, perhaps, absurd to others.
When he went from London to his estate of Belmont in
Scotland, it was his practice to walk round his park and
take off his hat to the trees he loved most. If Sir Henry
had been given to irony, it might be supposed that the
gesture was intended as a compliment on the company he
had left behind at Westminster. 'The more I see of men,'
he might have meant, adapting Pascal's famous phrase,
'the better I like trees.' But I do not fancy there was any
anger with men in his greeting. There was nothing of the
misanthrope in that shrewd and companionable man. He
was a good hater, and had as acute a sense of character as
any man of his time. He knew a crook or a humbug by
instinct, and anything fraudulent or shoddy withered in his
presence; but an honest, plain man was always at home
with him.

He saluted his favourite trees in the spirit in which
Xerxes, when passing with his army through Lydia, decorated with golden ornaments a plane tree of extraordinary
beauty, and left a warrior from the Immortal Band to be its
special guard, as you may read in Herodotus. He saluted
them because he loved them, and no one who has the spirit
of the woodlands in him will think the action odd or even
fanciful. It has never occurred to me to go about the woods
taking off my hat to the kings of the forest, but that only
shows that I have less imagination and less chivalry than
he had. I am not sure I shall not do so in future. It is the
last courtesy I can offer them for all the pleasure they have
given me in life, and the action will seem reasonable enough

E

to any one who has witnessed those wonderful experimen
of Professor Bhose which reveal the inner life of the tr
with such thrilling suggestions of consciousness and emotio

It is not possible to live much among trees without e
periencing a subtle sense of comradeship with them. O
intimacy may not go so far as that of Giles Winterbour
in *The Woodlanders*, who could tell what sort of trees he w
passing in the dark by the sound of the wind in the branch
—but without that erudition it can create an affectic
almost personal, not unlike that we feel for those quiet cor
panions of whom we have not thought much, perhaps, un
we find that their simple constancy and friendliness ha
made the atmosphere and sunshine in which we moved.

I confess that when I walk through the woods that crow
the hills behind the cottage, and see the great boles of tl
noblest of the beeches marked for felling, I feel very muc
as when I hear bad news of an old friend. That tho
glorious fellows, whom I have seen clothing themselves wi
green in the spring and with gold in the autumn, should l
brought low and split into fragments to make chairs ar
tables seems a sacrilege. It is an unpractical sentiment,
course, and I dare say if I owned the trees I should cut the
down, too. So I am glad I don't own them, and can ju
love them and lament them.

I should, however, find it hard to cut down beech trees
all trees, for after many affairs of the heart with trees, n
affections have settled finally on them as the pride of o
English woodlands. With what stateliness they spring fro
the ground, how noble their shade, how exquisite the gre
of their leaves in spring, how rich the gold of autumn, wh
a glowing carpet they spread for us in winter! If I go
Epping Forest it is to see the grand patriarchs of the tri
who are gathered together in solemn conclave in Monl
Wood, and if I place Buckinghamshire high among t
counties, it is because there you will find a more abunda
wealth of beeches than anywhere else in the land.

But I am no narrow sectarian about trees. If I put the
beech first, I worship at many shrines. When I go to
Chenies it is to pay my devotions to the Duke of Bedford's
oaks, and especially the aforesaid Queen Elizabeth's oak,
which still strews the greensward with acorns, though in its
ancient trunk, hollowed by the centuries, you could seat a
tolerably large tea-party. And who would go to Shere
without a visit to those stalwart Spanish chestnuts that are
the glory of the Duke of Northumberland's park? It is
worth a journey to Salisbury, not merely to see the spire and
Stonehenge, but to make the acquaintance of those magnificent cedars in Wilton Park. There is an elm at Nuneham
that I go to see much as I go to see a venerable relative, and
there is a wonderful yew tree in the churchyard of Tidworth
in Surrey that is better worth a pilgrimage than many a
cathedral.

A. G. GARDINER.

## The Poplar-field

THE poplars are fell'd, farewell to the shade
And the whispering sound of the cool colonnade,
The winds play no longer, and sing in the leaves,
Nor Ouse on his bosom their image receives.

Twelve years have elaps'd since I first took a view
Of my favourite field and the bank where they grew,
And now in the grass behold they are laid,
And the tree is my seat that once lent me a shade.

The blackbird has fled to another retreat
Where the hazels afford him a screen from the heat,
And the scene where his melody charm'd me before,
Resounds with his sweet-flowing ditty no more.

My fugitive years are all hasting away,
And I must ere long lie as lowly as they,
With a turf on my breast, and a stone at my head,
Ere another such grove shall arise in its stead.

'Tis a sight to engage me, if any thing can,
To muse on the perishing pleasures of man;
Though his life be a dream, his enjoyments, I see,
Have a being less durable even than he.

WILLIAM COWPER.

# Trees

WE all have our favourite trees, and my first friend was the
early apple in the corner of the orchard. Its fruit ripened
just before the Quarantines, and the tree was usually stripped
before we went back to school. Other apples came and
went during those dreadful thirteen weeks when orchard
and apple-lofts were out of bounds, but at Christmas the
Blenheim Orange was at its best, and no schoolboy has seen
a handsomer sight than a dish of ripe Blenheims.

Later on, I transferred my affections to the low slanting
willow tree in which the rock-pigeons built, and later still
to the tall elm with its magpie's nest, but the apple was my
first love. There was the further advantage that it figured
in those old stories of spacious days when golden apples
grew in the garden of the Hesperides, and lovely ladies con-
tended in that first beauty show for the glittering prize.
And there was the wild crab-apple in the big double hedge
with its lashings of sour fruit, to say nothing of those nondescript old trees on which the mistletoe grew and in which
the 'mistletoe thrush' built its nest.

But these were adventitious aids to youthful enthusiasm

nd of all the trees I have loved for themselves alone, the
ime must be given pride of place. A little sweet, a trifle
ticky, and apt to be over-sentimentalized perhaps, but on
ι warm day, when the bees are busy, the lime tree takes a
ot of beating. The trouble with the lime tree is that it
nust be well cut back every few years, and when this is
done, there is always a terrific outcry from stupid people.
f you know the lovely old town of Burford in Oxfordshire
ʊou will remember that the famous hill is flanked by a double
ow of lime trees. Just recently these had got so out of
ιand that they were cut 'back to the bone,' and presented,
»ne must admit, a sorry spectacle. There was such a
umpus that a London paper appeared with a photograph
ɔf those naked lime trees, and the city fathers who had done
he deed were covered with almost national opprobrium.
Γhey suffered in silence, but the next spring, when pale
ʒreen leaves showed against the black branches, they were
horoughly justified.

Then there is the poplar—a graceful tree which grows
ιlmost as quickly as the elder. At its prime the poplar is
ι lovely thing, but its prime is soon past, and it then looks
ike a windmill with three of the sweeps missing. Where
he river Thames is joined, just above Lechlade, by its first
ributary, there is a round house once surrounded by a ring
»f poplars. Not a landscape artist of the 'eighties who did
ιot make the journey to paint those poplar trees. But
ʋhere are they now?

If your cottage is in the shadow of chalk hills, your life
ʋill be dominated by beech trees, and you may learn to love
hem the best of all. Beech leaves make an excellent
nattress, and keep fresh for seven or eight years. Such a
nattress is known as a poke, and hardy hikers who sleep
ough will find it as good as a feather bed. The first night
slept on one I filled the sack too full, and spent the night
ʋrestling with its damned convexity. But I couldn't blame
he beech leaves for that.

And so we might ramble on among the trees which I hope will be your friendly companions during your happy exile in the country.

If I were asked to state, in a few words, what the country means to me, I should say this:

Deep down in the heart of every Englishman is the desire to be his own master: to live in his own house, to work in his own garden, to make his own friends, and to live comfortably within his modest means. City life, to-day, offers none of these things. Our energies are spent in maintaining the circulation of money. Like the donkey with the carrot, we must be for ever striving to secure phantom pleasures that always escape us. As a forgotten cynic wrote:

> We squander health in search of wealth;
>   We scheme and toil and save:
> Then squander wealth in search of health,
>   And only find a grave. . . .

And all the time, just over the hill, a simpler and happier life, well within our means, is beckoning us. The country offers us time to think, leisure to observe, kindly neighbours and a garden in which to work and dream. Along the lane in summer, the wild dog-rose wastes a sweeter perfume than was ever bottled in all the scent factories of the south. Winter brings the cheerful smell of wood fires and stored apples.

Here is a way of escape. Why not take it?

REGINALD ARKELL, *A Cottage in the Country*.

# 4. Roads

# The Reddleman

HE marched resolutely along, and found nothing to alarm him till, coming within a few yards of the sandpit, he heard a slight noise in front, which led him to halt. The halt was but momentary, for the noise resolved itself into the steady bites of two animals grazing.

'Two he'th-croppers down here,' he said aloud. 'I have never known 'em come down so far afore.'

The animals were in the direct line of his path, but that the child thought little of; he had played round the fetlocks of horses from his infancy. On coming nearer, however, the boy was somewhat surprised to find that the little creatures did not run off, and that each wore a clog, to prevent his going astray; this signified that they had been broken in. He could now see the interior of the pit, which, being in the side of the hill, had a level entrance. In the innermost corner the square outline of a van appeared, with its back towards him. A light came from the interior, and threw a moving shadow upon the vertical face of gravel at the further side of the pit into which the vehicle faced.

The child assumed that this was the cart of a gipsy, and his dread of those wanderers reached but to that mild pitch which titillates rather than pains. Only a few inches of mud wall kept him and his family from being gipsies themselves. He skirted the gravel-pit at a respectful distance, ascending the slope, and came forward upon the brow, in order to look into the open door of the van and see the original of the shadow.

The picture alarmed the boy. By a little stove inside the van sat a figure red from head to heels—the man who had been Thomasin's friend. He was darning a stocking, which was red like the rest of him. Moreover, as he darned he smoked a pipe, the stem and bowl of which were red also.

At this moment one of the heath-croppers feeding in the outer shadows was audibly shaking off the clog attached to its foot. Aroused by the sound, the reddleman laid down his stocking, lit a lantern which hung beside him, and came out from the van. In sticking up the candle he lifted the lantern to his face, and the light shone into the whites of his eyes and upon his ivory teeth, which, in contrast with the red surrounding, lent him a startling aspect enough to the gaze of a juvenile. The boy knew too well for his peace of mind upon whose lair he had lighted. Uglier persons than gipsies were known to cross Egdon at times, and a reddleman was one of them.

'How I wish 'twas only a gipsy!' he murmured.

The man was by this time coming back from the horses. In his fear of being seen the boy rendered detection certain by nervous motion. The heather and peat stratum overhung the brow of the pit in mats, hiding the actual verge. The boy had stepped beyond the solid ground; the heather now gave way, and down he rolled over the scarp of grey sand to the very foot of the man.

The red man opened the lantern and turned it upon the figure of the prostrate boy.

'Who be ye?' he said.

'Johnny Nunsuch, master!'

'What were you doing up there?'

'I don't know.'

'Watching me, I suppose?'

'Yes, master.'

'What did you watch me for?'

'Because I was coming home from Miss Vye's bonfire.'

'Beest hurt?'

'No.'

'Why, yes, you be: your hand is bleeding. Come under my tilt and let me tie it up.'

'Please let me look for my sixpence.'

'How did you come by that?'

'Miss Vye gied it to me for keeping up her bonfire.'

The sixpence was found, and the man went to the van, the boy behind, almost holding his breath.

The man took a piece of rag from a satchel containing sewing materials, tore off a strip, which, like everything else, was tinged red, and proceeded to bind up the wound.

'My eyes have got foggy-like—please may I sit down, master?' said the boy.

'To be sure, poor chap. ''Tis enough to make you feel fainty. Sit on that bundle.'

The man finished tying up the gash, and the boy said: 'I think I'll go home now, master.'

'You are rather afraid of me. Do you know what I be?'

The child surveyed his vermilion figure up and down with much misgiving, and finally said, 'Yes.'

'Well, what?'

'The reddleman!' he faltered.

'Yes, that's what I be. Though there's more than one. You little children think there's only one cuckoo, one fox, one giant, one devil, and one reddleman, when there's lots of us all.'

'Is there? You won't carry me off in your bags, will ye, master? 'Tis said that the reddleman will sometimes.'

'Nonsense. All that reddlemen do is sell reddle. You see all these bags at the back of my cart? They are not full of little boys—only full of red stuff.'

'Was you born a reddleman?'

'No, I took to it. I should be as white as you if I were to give up the trade—that is, I should be white in time—perhaps six months: not at first, because 'tis grow'd into my skin and won't wash out. Now, you'll never be afraid of a reddleman again, will ye?'

THOMAS HARDY, *The Return of the Native.*

# Turnpikes

OF all the roads that ever disgraced this kingdom, in the
very ages of barbarism, none ever equalled that from Billericay to the King's Head at Tilbury. It is for nearly
twelves miles so narrow, that a mouse cannot pass by any
carriage; I saw a fellow creep under his wagon to assist me
to lift, if possible, my chaise over a hedge. The rutts are
of an incredible depth—and a pavement of diamonds might
as well be fought for as a quarter. The trees everywhere
overgrow the road, so that it is totally impervious to the sun,
except at a few places: And to add to all the infamous circumstances, which concur to plague a traveller, I must not
forget eternally meeting with chalk - wagons; themselves
frequently stuck fast, till a collection of them are in the
same situation, that twenty or thirty horses may be tacked
to each, to draw them out one by one.

After this description, will you—can you believe me when
I tell you, that a turnpike was much solicited by some
gentlemen, to lead from Chelmsford to the ferry at Tilbury
fort, but opposed by the bruins of this country—whose
horses are worried to death with bringing chalk through
these vile roads. I do not imagine that the kingdom pro-
duces such an instance of detestable stupidity; and yet in
this tract are found numbers of farmers, who cultivate above
1000 l. a year. Besides those already mentioned, we find
a Skinner and a Towers, who each rent near 1500 l. a year,
and a Read almost equal; but who are all perfectly well
contented with their roads.

I forgot to tell you, that near Horndon, on the summit
of a vast hill, one of the most astonishing prospects to be
beheld, breaks almost at once upon one of the dark lanes.
Such a prodigious valley, every where painted with the finest

[CRUMMOCK WATER

verdure, and intersected with numberless hedges and woods, appears beneath you, that it is past description; the Thames winding thro' it, full of ships, and bounded by the hills of Kent. Nothing can exceed it, unless that which Hannibal exhibited to his disconsolate troops, when he bade them behold the glories of the Italian plains! If ever a turnpike should lead through this country, I beg you will go and view this enchanting scene, though a journey of 40 miles is necessary for it. I never beheld any thing equal to it in the West of England, that region of landscape.

I chiefly travelled upon turnpikes; all of which, that from Salisbury, to four miles the other side of Rumsey, towards Winchester, is, without exception, the finest I ever saw. The trustees of that road, highly deserve all the praise that can be given, by every one who travels it, for their excellent management: to management the goodness of it must be owing; for fine as their materials are, yet I have in other counties met with as fine; but never with any that were so firmly united, and kept so totally free from loose stones, ruts and water; and, when I add water, let me observe, that it is not by that vile custom of cutting grips for it to run off, to the dislocation of one's bones in crossing them, and to the utter destruction of all common beauty resulting from level-ness; but by rendering the surface so immoveably firm, that carriages make no holes for it to settle in; and having every-where a gentle fall, it runs immediately off. To conclude the whole it is every where broad enough for three carriages to pass each other; and lying in straight lines, with an even edge of grass the whole way, it has more the appearance of an elegant gravel walk, than of a high-road.

Next to this uncommon road, the great north one to Barnet, I think, must be ranked. Then the Kentish one: and the others to Chelmsford and Uxbridge succeed. Next I rank the 18 miles of finished road, from Cowbridge in Glamorganshire, to six miles this side of Cardiff. As to all the rest, it is a prostitution of language to call them turn-pikes; I rank them nearly in the same class, with the dark lanes from Billericay to Tilbury fort. Among the bad ones however, some parts of the road from Tetsford to Gloucester are much better than the unmended parts from Gloucester to the good road above-mentioned, on this side of Cardiff. The latter is all terrible; but then it is a great extenuation to observe that they have been at work but two years. Much more to be condemned, is the execrable muddy road from Bury to Sudbury in Suffolk; in which I was forced to move as slow as in any unmended lane in Wales: For ponds or liquid dirt, and a scattering of loose flints, just sufficient to lame every horse that moves near them, with the addition of cutting vile grips across the road, under pretence of letting water off, but without the effect,[1] all together render, at least, 12 out of these 16 miles, as infamous a turnpike as ever was travelled.—The road likewise from Chelmsford to Hedingham, though not so bad, is something in the same stile; which is the more disagreeable, as it used to be much better. As to Norfolk and her *natural roads*, the boast of the inhabitants, who repeat with vanity the saying of Charles II; all I have to remark is, that I know not one mile of excellent road in the whole county. One furlong upon the Salisbury turnpike, above mentioned, is worth all that nature or art has done for travellers, in the whole county of Norfolk. Bad, however, as all natural roads are, part of the Norfolk ones, it must be allowed, exceed the Suffolk turnpike

ARTHUR YOUNG, *A Six Weeks Tour through the Southern Counties of England and Wales.*

[1] The hacknied argument, that the water must be carried off, is of some force with regard to the bye roads, wherein the rutts are single-deep channels, but of none with turnpikes; for it is nonsense to pretend to call a road a turnpike one that lies so low in the center, or has rutts deep enough to require grips to let the water off; and unless the rutts are single and deep, as in cross-roads, grips may be cut for ever without effect; for where there is so much thick mud, they are eternally filling up again. The only way to lay a road dry is to have every where a gentle slope, and *no rutts*; for without these circumstances are effected the gates may take money from travellers, but will never give tolerable roads in return.

# On Knowing a Country

To know a country it is not enough to have seen some tit-bit of a place here and there. What do they know of England who only know Chester and Stratford-on-Avon, Warwick and Winchester, Oxford and Windsor? The land is the common run of the land, both the choice and the poor, barren place and fertile; everything that Caliban showed Prospero—'*all* the qualities o' th' isle.' And yet you must come to know them as things connected and truly parts of a whole. To this latter end there is no better means than to make friends with some one great trunk road. Get to know, for example, the road from London to Manchester, running through St Albans, Woburn, Northampton, Leicester, Derby and Buxton. That done, your knowledge of England will have a backbone, something central, columnar, and sturdy. Everything else that you come to know later will fall easily into its place as tissue attached to that spinal pillar.

What is it, though, that we mean here by 'knowing' a road? Not just seeing it all once or twice from a seat in a car and having it on the word of your own eyes that the southern Midlands are mainly grass land and the Peak country rocky. Nor yet need you learn it by heart, to the last house and tree, as children learn the few hundred yards of road to and from school. There is a mean—to know it as people soon come to know the daily way home from a new place of work. Of that you make no set study; you do not cram it up; rather you leave your mind merely ajar, to let in such ideas of it as may come. Try, when you are not upon it, to call the course of it up, and it comes back less like a continuous line than a row of dots, bright beads strung thinly on a dim string. Not the road so much as points upon the road have taken the mind—here a fine or an ugly church, there a tree with odd boles or a name on a shop;

yet, in a way, they are all joined; from each to the next your perception has moved as a climber on rock works from hold to hold, feeling back while reaching out, grasp passing into grasp, to be merged in the one act of adhesion made up of them all.

That is how to know a great road; you know it enough when you can shut your eyes, call up a row of points upon it, and feel how, as you went along, your senses only quitted their hold upon each when they had the next to fix on; how, say, as you set out from London for Manchester your eye travelled from Hampstead across the wide and deep dip to Finchley Church on its further bank, and then from Finchley over the next great trench to the knot of houses on the crest of High Barnet, and how from Barnet you traced the wooded line of Ridge Hill in the north-west, and, gaining Ridge Hill, just spied St Albans Minster on the horizon, picked out by its harder lines from the softly modelled woods that it seems to spring from. So the grasp that your senses have of the road is carried on to the end in a kind of rhythm, as you go the length of a gymnasium through the air by a row of hanging rings, just carried by the end of each swing into reach of the ring that waits for you next, to hand you on in its turn. To leave no gap ringless in your memory, to be able in bed at night to go over it all, nowhere at a loss for the next hold—that will suffice. And all the better if the holds be well spaced out, so that the mind must reach out with a will and the eye learn to look at country in the large, till it can see, or almost see, the Vale of Trent as a whole, or the oneness of the crumpled and worn arch of red sandstone and coal, millstone grit and mountain limestone over which you can ride a push-bicycle in a short day between Stockport and Derby.

C. E. MONTAGUE, *The Right Place.*

## The Idlers

THE gipsies lit their fires by the chalk-pit gate anew,
And the hoppled horses supped in the further dusk and dew;
The gnats flocked round the smoke like idlers as they were
And through the goss and bushes the owls began to churr.

An ell above the woods the last of sunset glowed
With a dusky gold that filled the pond beside the road;
The cricketers had done, the leas all silent lay,
And the carrier's clattering wheels went past and died away.

The gipsies lolled and gossiped, and ate their stolen swedes,
Made merry with mouth-organs, worked toys with piths of
    reeds:
The old wives puffed their pipes, nigh as black as their hair,
And not one of them all seemed to know the name of care.

EDMUND BLUNDEN, *Poems 1914–30*.

## Ancient Trackways

RIVERS and roads run often to-day side by side, as the
modern road from Epping to Cambridge follows the Stort
and the Cam; but this was not the ancient way. Most river-
valleys were too wet to be inhabited, and had no need of
roads. Before the Romans came to fling their great highways over hill and plain, most roads clung to the ridges or
the hillsides, and crossed the valleys where they were
narrowest. All the old roads of England, even the Roman
roads, have been dissected during centuries of disuse, and

F

partly abandoned and partly incorporated in fragmentary and piecemeal fashion into later highways and byways. But while the ancient hollow tracks that crept from spring to spring or from one pasture to another are perpetuated in a thousand country lanes, the oldest trails along the open hill-tops are mostly left desolate.

The most famous hill-track in England is the route from the dry chalk Hampshire Downs along the North Downs in Surrey to the hills about Canterbury. We call it the Pilgrims' Way, because it was followed in the Middle Ages by pilgrims travelling to the shrine of St Thomas at Canterbury from a large part of the south and west of England, and by others from abroad who landed at Southampton. But the name merely perpetuates its dying purpose. For unknown centuries before Thomas à Becket's time that dry chalk track overlooking the marshy river-bottoms must have been followed by all who moved from east to west, or west to east, through the southern seaboard counties. It is pre-historic, and a more ancient monument than any building.

This road presents both a likeness and a contrast with the second great prehistoric track of southern England—the Ridgeway or Icknield Way. This runs from the neigh-bourhood of Stonehenge along the northern crests of the chalk through Berkshire, and then, after crossing the Thames at the ford between Streatley and Goring, pursues its way by a less clearly marked line along the same chalk ridge past Royston and Newmarket into Norfolk. Between three and four thousand years ago that may have been a Pilgrims' Way too, if, as some hold, Stonehenge was a great national temple to which all the tribes of the chalk country flocked annually to a feast of the sun. But just as the southern Pilgrims' Way led traffic from the west into Kent, so the Ridgeway directed it into far-away Norfolk.

There is one outstanding difference in these ancient tracks. Part of the fascination of the Pilgrims' Way, as we trace it along the Surrey hills by Gomshall, and away past Shoreham into Kent, is that it clings either to the side of the hills, or to the dry ground just at their foot. It basks and nestles in the sunshine. But follow the Ridgeway westwards past the Streatley dovecot, up the long downs where the wheatears sing, and away along the smooth greensward of the Fair Mile above Aston and Blewbury. It is justly called the Ridgeway; we are treading the very crest of the Berkshire chalk, with a view far over Oxford into the Midlands.

Profound significance has been claimed for the fashion in which the Pilgrims' Way takes the side, and not the top, of the hills; while others have argued that to cling to the south side of the range is a general feature of these old highways. A few days spent in comparing the two routes and the two ranges will clear up our views. The Pilgrims' Way provides a reasonably easy and unbroken route along the side of the Kent and Surrey hills, because they throw out a few spurs with intervening valleys. The crest of the hills faces south, and this gives the additional advantage of a sheltered and sunny aspect. Turn to Berkshire, and the conditions are reversed. The crest of the hills faces north, and spur after spur thrusts north too, with deep intervening valleys. The road at the downs' foot from Streatley to Wantage is a continuous series of steep switchbacks, and the lateral ridges and furrows do not vanish until close under the crest of the ridge. Far westward it still picks its way along the highest ground, for the combes of the dry streams cut up the landscape as it slopes to the south, and debar the road from seeking shelter and sunshine.

Beneath both these ancient tracks, which for the most part remain as green unmetalled lanes, there is a road at a few hundred yards' distance which keeps closely parallel. In Berkshire it is called the Port Way, and the name of the Icknield Way is sometimes transferred to it.

ANTHONY COLLETT, *The Changing Face of England.*

## The Drive in the Snowstorm

GLAD as he was to be turned for home, Merry-Grig was gladder. As he turned out of the farmyard into the lane, he realized that he was driving within a few points of the wind's eye. The pellets of hard snow were falling into his face, especially upon his left cheek. There were not many of them yet, but they were more than they had been a few minutes before. 'They 'll be troublesome to drive through, if they get much worse,' he said. 'And they 're going to be much worse. I don't think I ever saw a more hideous-looking sky.' By the little clock in front of him he saw the time: twenty-five minutes to four.

The evil of the air smote into him as he drove, while the pellets increased in number minute by minute. He was not conscious of any wind, yet most of the pellets struck, as it seemed, from the one point, slantingly across his face. Soon the road, which had been soft that morning, bore a powdering of white, and became crisper under the wheels, while from minute to minute the numbers of the pellets increased with the variety of their direction. It was then bad going, for the snow balled hard on the hoofs, and was slippery.

Presently, as he drove, he felt an urge in the air (more of an impulse of the storm than wind), in which the snow pellets increased from many into multitude. They came at him now from all points, they came patting ceaselessly upon his face, pecking at his eyes, and getting down his collar. Bent as he was, with his hat jammed down upon his brow, he found it difficult to see to drive. It was fast becoming dark. The snow was now falling in such quantity that often he could not see the hedge by the roadside. It was a lonely road at the best of times: he saw no living soul. 'Hold on a minute, old boy,' he said to his horse. 'Come back

here; stop . . . I 'll have to light my lamps.   Come: stop you.'

He had some difficulty in tying the horse, who wanted to get home.   The snow was already deep on the road. There was not yet any sensible wind, but just in front of where he stopped a drift was floating over the road across a gap in the hedge.   This drift looked like a living person, or procession of persons, with a purpose; it advanced and advanced.   'I don't know where the devil I 've got to,' he said, 'I suppose this is somewhere about the Gray Sisters, a mile the wrong side of "Tod and Tickler."   I 'm making bad time: the poor beast slips so.   It 'll be no joke on the Godsdown.'

He contrived to get his lamps lit; and what was harder, to hold Merry-Grig while he got back into the trap.   Again he set out into the storm, which was now dark with the multitude of the falling flakes and threatening an utter dark-ness.   He heard the scrunch of the snow balling on Merry-Grig's feet, the jingle of the harness, the muffled noise of the wheels, and a sort of moan in the air.   Every now and then Merry-Grig slipped a little: then he would chuck him up with the rein and call to him.   He was a good, game, strong young horse, eager to get home.   'Come along, good boy,' George kept saying.   'Up now, come up, old son.'   But eager as he was, the going was all slip and shuffle.

.          .          .          .          .

After half an hour of this, George felt the storm gather markedly in might, and drive against them with a multi-tudinous power that took away the heart.   'Now, old boy,' he said to the horse; 'this is something we can hardly make head against.   And I 'm afraid I 've led you wrong.   We ought to have reached Cheddlesdon Turn by this.   Where on this wide earth are we?'

He bethought him of a little compass which hung from his watch chain.   It was a poor little thing, but by the light of the lamp it showed him that he was heading south. 'That is how the road runs,' he said. 'And the wind is a bit to the east of that. We may be right: but where is the Turn? And then, there are those barrows near the road. Surely, I should see them?'

There was no seeing anything except multitudinous flying fragments coming inexhaustibly out of darkness into his lamplight. The strain of trying to see, in that whirl of snow, which beat continually into the eyes, was the thing that quenched the spirit.

'It's no good stopping,' George said. 'We must get on; every step counts. Stopping only wastes good strength.'

They crawled on for another quarter of a mile without coming to any telegraph posts. Then suddenly, with a sidelong slither and crash, the horse, George, and the trap went over into a deeply drifted ditch. The near light was instantly quenched in snow, and the near shaft snapped.

George was dragged down by the horse, but kept a tight hold of the rein, and kept the horse's head down. He floundered in a sort of pit of snow until he found a footing. Merry-Grig's feet were scraping wildly for foothold.

'Keep still, you old fool,' he said. He sat on the horse's head and groped with his wet hands into sodden pockets for his knife.

As he tried to open the blade, to cut the horse free, there came a kind of glee into the storm. It ran at him as at a mark, heaping and twisting the whiteness about him as though to engulf and smother. 'You're very strong,' it seemed to say, 'but you are only one, and we are many, many, many: we are going to be too many for you.' He saw, as it were, slabs of it cake over his remaining lamp. 'By Jove,' he muttered, 'if I don't get up and get the horse up pretty soon, I do believe we may be done for.' He spat the snow out of his mouth and got to work. 'By Jove,' he said, 'snow's not going to beat me, nor get my horse.' He groped for leather after leather and cut it through, going over them in order in his mind.   A struggle from the horse at one point knocked the knife out of his hand, so that he had to grope for it in the snow.   'Jove, this *is* a lovely night!' he said.   'A real spring evening.'

As he groped and hove and cut, he felt that he was like a half-tide rock, with flood advancing.   There came as it were, sudden leaps or runs of snow, which gathered as they sped, burst upon him, and flung their spray.   Snow heaped against him as sand heaps against a wreck in a tide-way.   'Now, if this old fool bolts,' George said, 'he'll find soft falling wherever he comes down next.   You're clear now, old son; so up you come: stand up.'   He hove and cheered, and got him to his feet.   The horse swayed and surged as though about to bolt.   'Quiet, old boy,' George said.   'It's all right.   It's all right.'   The horse whinnied and instead of trying to bolt, shied back into the drift. George got him back on to the road, and with his left hand scraped the snow from the lamp.   'What's the matter, old son?' he said.   'There, old man. Cheer up now, calm yourself.'   The horse was in terror and trembling; and some of the terror passed into George.

He did not reach home until daylight.   The storm is still spoken of in those parts as 'The Fury.'

JOHN MASEFIELD, *The Hawbucks*.

# Decline of the English Inn

MUCH unkind criticism has been levelled at the British inn-keeper, but there are two sides to every question. Tragic must have been his lot and difficult his problem when, about seventy years before motoring appeared, stage-coach and post-chaise traffic was ruined by the coming of the railways.

Consequent upon that, the bed-and-board part of inn-keeping went to sleep for half a century.

Think what this meant! All the happy clatter of arrival and departure gone. The stables empty. Drivers and guards and ostlers and waiters and serving maids on the unemployed list, with no dole. The hay-and-corn-chandler bankrupt. The butcher and baker and candlestick-maker going much the same way. The turnspit silent. Beds and blankets and glassware and cutlery no longer needed—often sold off at beggarly prices to help pay the rent and keep things going. All that cheery noise and bustle portrayed so delightfully by Dickens fading into oblivion.

Thereafter the roadside inn had perforce to shrink within itself, dependent for its owner's meagre existence upon the villager's capacity for liquor and the chance custom of a commercial traveller, known then as a bagman.

Here, surely, was a sickness approaching unto death, from which it seemed hardly possible for an industry to recover.

Let us imagine the scene, somewhere on the Great North Road, one evening in autumn. A sad little group is gathered round the porch of the Duke's Arms, waiting for the stage-coach, due almost any minute now, to pull up, change horses, and pass on her final stage—for the last time. For years this beautiful, lovable, living thing, with horses, coach, coachman, and guard complete, one and indivisible, has swung round the bend and pulled up, all standing, to the tick. 'Set your watch by the Duchess? You can, sir—ay—danged if you can't!'

The horn which heralds her arrival sounds a bit cracked. The guard may have a lump in his throat. He isn't the only one.

'Whoa, my beauties!' Ostlers run to their heads, reins are handed down over the whip, off the box steps Sam the coachman, into the cosy bar for his usual rum and water with the landlord—for the last time.

'And to think that this is the end!' says Sam. 'When we get to Nottingham to-night, and stable the team, it 'll be for the last time—and to-morrow! nothing, nothing but selling off the horses and coach and gear. Thirty years on this road, man and boy, and now! What 's to become of us?'

'Poor Sam!' sighs the landlord. 'Never mind—you 're not the only one. What 's to become of us? How long the poor old Duke 's Arms is going to last when you 've gone I don 't know. Bad luck to that Scotchman who thought of steam engines.'

'Time, gentlemen! Passengers aboard, please. Shake hands, Sam; come and see us soon. Always a welcome for you. Good-bye—good-bye!'

The beautiful, lovable, living thing, nearly empty, is all ready for her last stage. It is a solemn moment. The horses stand quite still. They seem to know.

Every one is silent. Something is passing from the gentle life of this little English village, never to return. The church clock chimes the quarter. That breaks the spell. Sam the coachman pulls himself together and barks to the guard: 'Sound! Joe, dang you, man—sound!'

Joe does his poor best. A few try to cheer, and give it up. The women cry quietly. Sam twirls his whip, game to the end, and clucks a command. The team obey as one horse, and the Duchess, queen of the stage-coach realm, rumbles

away down, down, down the road into the limbo of things
forgotten.

Think what that meant!

.   .        .        .        .        .

It softens the lump in one's throat to reflect that new
life was brought back to the innkeeping industry by This
Motoring.

That last lost chord of Joe the guard, which had trembled
away into silence, was to speak again in the honk-honk of a
motor car, pulling up at the old Duke's Arms for refreshment
of man and engine.

The pneumatic tyre was restoring what the iron wheel
had killed.

'Mary!' cried the third generation of the Duke's Arms to
his wife; 'it's wonderful! Here's life and hope coming
back to the old house—in motor cars. Just think of it
five of 'em stopped here to-day and we've served fourteen
meals. Never mind if they *do* smell different from horses
Here they are, I tell you, waking up the road, waking us all
up. New life, business—coming back. It is good enough
to make Grandfather turn in his grave. Bustle, Mary
We must show 'em that we know our business. Fancy
the old times coming back! coming——'

'Yes, John! and now stop talking and start working,
replied his very much better half. 'You must do something
more than hang about in the bar parlour. These new folk
will expect clean tablecloths and new cutlery, and napkins
to wipe their fingers on. And good beds and blankets and
sheets—sheets, mind you, changed for every customer
That and about fifty other things will be my department
The Lord send we can borrow the money to buy them
Your job is to talk straight to the butcher and get more
credit—make him understand what all this may mean to
him as well as us. Then to the baker, and greengrocer
Make them understand, too! Then go along to the brewer

—they ought to give us an extra loan, enough to buy all the things we want for the house. It means quite as much to them as it does to us. And another thing: these people will want motor spirit, petrol—or something like that—instead of hay and corn. The stables aren't much use, but the coach-houses can be turned into a—what's that French word, John? There seems to be a lot of French in this new business.'

'It's "garage," Mary. I saw in one of those new motor papers——'

'Yes! that's it—and—there we go again, what do they call the men who drive?'

'Chaffours, or something like that!'

'Yes! Well we must have a special room for them, like Grandfather had for the post-boys and grooms; that's very much what they are, really, in spite of their outlandish name. We shall soon be having to get some more maids. And who knows, we may be able to afford a real waiter again! Oh! there's a lot to be done.'

SIR STENSON COOKE, *This Motoring.*

# The English Roads

THE history of the English road, between the time of the Romans and the nineteenth century, is a history of neglect and decay. Little was done to preserve the Roman surfaces, and few new roads were planned; the roads, except in the driest of weather, became broken and muddy and dangerous to the traffic they threatened to engulf. If the movements and the rate of movement of the medieval army surprise us, we have to remember that the rate of march of an army with its wagons was unbelievably slow, and that transporting a force of any size across a bridge or over a ford was a matter of hours and not of minutes. Legislation concerning the roads is rare in medieval times; the best-known specimen is Edward I's ordinance that from both sides of the highway the brushwood should be cleared and robbers thus deprived of their place of ambush. As late as 1640 it took three days to journey by wheeled transport from London to Dover, and in 1751 the journey from London to Exeter took four days; the effort of reaching Oxford from London in a single day was in 1669 considered remarkable. Six years previously the first Turnpike Act had been passed, with the idea of making users of the roads contribute to their upkeep by paying tolls for the right of passage. To this system we owe the numerous tracks within easy distance of the old main roads; drovers of cattle and sheep, unwilling to pay the tolls, made their own paths on the hillside, and the impress of their charges' feet has remained. As I write this in December 1936 there are still sixty-six bridges to cross for which a toll has to be paid, and fifty-seven roads subject to toll, three of these being in the London area.

Though the great years of English roadmaking are properly the last half of the eighteenth century, the chief era of the stage and the mail coaches is of an even later date. It must be remembered that railway succeeded coach transport quite soon after the latter had attained its zenith, and that the period made so familiar to us by Dickens was really quite a short one. It could not have developed as it did without the English road-makers, 'Blind Jack' Metcalf of Knaresborough, Macadam the descendant of Highland freebooters, whose method of road-surfacing enriched the English language by a new word, and the engineer Telford, who planned many of the new roads originating with this period. On what a scale English road traffic once was can be imagined from the fact that the village of Hounslow provided stabling accommodation for two thousand five hundred horses. In an age when England was inadequately policed such slow and cumbersome transport was the thief's opportunity.

Few of the classic highwaymen engage our sympathy, for they were mostly blackguards and cowards rather than creatures of romance, but few rural districts are without their legends and memories of a local or national 'gentleman of the road' who stopped the coaches and chaises and robbed the traveller of his belongings.

So great a volume of traffic gave great importance to the village and provincial city inns. Under such a system, with its mail coaches and passenger coaches, its private and public chaises, it was necessary for every village inn to provide some kind of accommodation in the way of board, lodging, and stabling, for accidents were so frequent, delays so likely, and the day's journey so short that none could in the morning say with certainty where he would sleep that night. In these days we are apt to consider a temporary cessation of railway traffic as something of an event, but there is a good deal of difference in the power of a locomotive and of a team of horses to cope with the effect of bad weather. Floods, in those days of badly-drained roads, must have been more frequent than they are now; cold, snow, and tempest of more effect than is recognized by the habitual traveller by train. The inn was the traveller's haven of refuge, ranged round its courtyard into which vehicles drove right up to its very door. Many of the old coaching inns have suffered considerable change, but the 'New Inn' at Gloucester, the 'George' at Winchester, and the 'George' at Huntingdon, particularly the first-named, still give a good idea of the nineteenth-century coaching inn.

REX WELLDON FINN, *The English Heritage.*

THE GEORGE, NORTON ST PHILIP]

# 5. Places

# The Cotswolds

CHIPPING CAMPDEN has a population of about one thousand five hundred, but it is a town and no village. It used to be a very prosperous town, the centre of the Cotswold wool trade and, later, of its silk manufacture. The whole of this region, though it seems now so Arcadian, is actually a depressed industrial area. It was once famous for its textiles. It had the wool, just as it has to-day; it had water power and plenty of soft water for dyeing; it had a good local supply of fuller's earth in the hillsides; and it was not far from the port of Bristol. The western area of the Cotswolds made broadcloth, which our grandfathers recognized as the best of all clothing fabrics. The other districts had their own specialities. To this day the best blankets come from Witney, just off the eastern edge of the Cotswolds. Even as late as 1801 a map of England showing the density of population includes this region in its most heavily shaded areas, with an average density of more than a hundred to the square mile. A similar map of modern England shows the bigger part of the region in its most lightly shaded division, with an average density of less than one hundred and twenty-eight persons to the square mile. There must be a great many districts that actually had far more people living in them in the Middle Ages than they have to-day, though now, when the road is rapidly triumphing over its former conqueror, the railway, many of those districts are beginning to fill up again. It was steam power, with its large-scale plants and reliance upon coal, that packed people together, herding them into hundreds of narrow streets. If there had been a few thick seams of coal between Gloucester, Evesham, and Cirencester, the Cotswolds would have been torn up and blackened and built over with brick horrors, and would now be enjoying an industrial depression far worse than anything it knew when steam power arrived to rob it of its ancient trade. As it is, the Cotswolds is singularly remote even from the railway, for only one line finds its way across these hills. It had its depression before the railway came, and no doubt had its painful problems too, with one little mill after another, one merchant after another, going out of business. But all that now is like an old bad dream. And there is Chipping Campden, not at all the important town it was when William Grevel built his house in the High Street, but exquisite in the sunlight, with no tall brick chimneys, no rows of hovels, no crowds of workless men. It went out of business at the right time and so escaped the grand uglification. That it has also escaped the new uglifying processes, which belong to our age, is not an accident. The credit must be given to one or two of its citizens, notably Mr F. L. Griggs, the artist, who has spent time, energy, and money for the last twenty-five years, keeping the place beautiful. Now, after a hard fight, the people themselves are ready to protect their town, which fortunately is still a real little town and not simply a show place and glorified tea establishment for tourists. There is no Ye Olde Chipping Campden nonsense about it.

When you look at the curved wide main street, you feel that such an unusual and exquisite harmony of line and colour in architecture could only have come from one particular period, almost from one particular mind. The secret, however, is that these Cotswold towns and villages and manor houses are the products of definite tradition. They were not all built at one time. Some buildings are hundreds of years older than their neighbours. But the tradition persisted. Houses were always built of certain material in a certain way. If you told a Cotswold man to build you a house, this is how he built it. He knew—thank God—no other way of building houses. This tradition has lasted until our own time. There are still some old Cotswold masons who work in that tradition and could work in no other. In their hands the stone flowers naturally into those mullions. They can see Cotswold houses already stirring in the very quarries. I say these men still exist, but there are not many of them and they grow old and feeble.

I was introduced to old George, a Cotswold mason. He is in his seventies but still at it. When I met him he was engaged in the almost lost art of dry-walling, pulling down some ramshackle old walls and converting their materials into smooth solid ramparts. He was a little man, with a dusty puckered face and an immense upper lip so that he looked like a wise old monkey; and he had spent all his long life among stones. There were bits of stone all over him. He handled the stones about him, some of which he showed to us, at once easily and lovingly, as women handle their babies. He was like a being that had been created out of stone, a quarry gnome. He was a pious man, this old George, and when he was not talking about stone and walls, he talked in a very quiet though evangelical strain about his religious beliefs, which were old and simple. Being a real craftsman, knowing that he could do something better than you or I could do it, he obviously enjoyed his work, which was not so much toil exchanged for so many shillings but the full expression of himself, his sign that he was Old George the mason and still at it. Bad walls, not of his building, were coming down, and good walls were going up. The stones in them fitted squarely and smoothly and were a delight to the eye and a great contentment to the mind, so weary of shoddy and rubbish. I have never done anything in my life so thoroughly and truly as that old mason did his building. If I could write this book, or any other book, as well as he can build walls, honest dry walls, I should be the proudest and happiest man alive. Old George has always been a mason, and his father and grandfather were masons before him; they were all masons, these Georges; they built the whole Cotswolds: men of their hands, men with a trade, craftsmen. I do not know for what pittances they worked, or how narrow and frugal their lives must have been, but I do know that they were not unhappy men; they knew what they could do and they were allowed to do it; they were not taught algebra and chemistry and then flung into a world that did not even want their casual labour; they were not robbed of all the dignity and sweetness of real work; they did not find themselves lost and hopeless in a world that neither they nor any one else could understand; they did not feel themselves to be tiny cogs in a vast machine that was running down; they had a good trade in their fingers, solid work to do, and when it was done—and there it was, with no mistake about it, ready to outlast whole dynasties —they could take their wages and go home and be content. I am glad I met old George and saw him at work. And if ever we do build Jerusalem in this green and pleasant land I hope he will be there, doing the dry-walling.

J. B. PRIESTLEY, *English Journey*.

# Halifax

WHEN this trade began to settle, nothing was more frequent than for young workmen to leave their cloths out all night upon the tenters, and the idle fellows would come in upon them, and tearing them off without notice, steal the cloth. Now as it was absolutely necessary to preserve the trade in its infancy, this severe law was made, giving the power of life and death so far into the hands of the magistrates of Halifax, as to see the law executed upon them. As this law was particularly pointed against the stealing of cloth, and no other crime, so no others were capable of being punished by it, and the conditions of the law intimate as

[THE MARKET HOUSE, CHIPPING CAMPDEN

much; for the power was not given to the magistrates to give sentence, unless in one of these three plain cases.

1. Hand napping, that is, to be taken in the very fact, or, as the Scots call it in the case of murther, red hand.

2. Back bearing, that is, when the cloth was found on the person carrying it off.

3. Tongue confessing, that part needs no farther explanation.

This being the case, if the criminal was taken, he was brought before the magistrates of the town, who at that time were only a baily and the eoaldermen, how many we do not read, and these were to judge, and sentence, and execute the offender, or clear him, within so many days. The country people were, it seems, so terrified at the severity of this proceeding, that hence came that proverbial saying, which was used all over Yorkshire, (viz.)

> From Hell, Hull, and Halifax,
> Good Lord deliver us.

How Hull came to be included in this petition, I do not find; for they had no such law there, as I read of.

The manner of execution was very remarkable; the engine indeed is carried away, but the scaffold on which it stood is there to this time, and may continue many ages; being not a frame of wood, but a square building of stone, with stone steps to go up, and the engine itself was made in the following manner.

They tell us of a custom which prevailed here, in the case of a criminal being to be executed, (viz.) that if after his head was laid down, and the signal given to pull out the pin, he could be so nimble as to snatch out his head between the pulling out the pin and the falling down of the ax, and could get up upon his feet, jump off of the scaffold, run down a hill that lies just before it, and get through the river before the executioner could overtake him, and seize upon him, he was to escape; and though the executioner did take him on the other side the river, he was not to bring him back, at least he was not to be executed.

But as they shewed me the form of the scaffold, and the weight of the ax, it was, in my opinion, next to impossible, any man should be so quick-eyed as to see the pulling out the pin and so quick with his head, as to snatch it out; yet they tell a story of one fellow that did it, and was so bold after he had jumpt off of the scaffold, and was running down the hill, with the executioner at his heels, to turn about and call to the people to give him his hat; that having afterwards jumpt into the river, which is but a little one, and not deep, he stopt, intending to drown the hangman, if he had come up to him; at which the poor fellow stopt too, and was afraid to go into the water to seize him.

DANIEL DEFOE, *A Tour of England and Wales.*

## Westminster Bridge

EARTH has not anything to show more fair:
Dull would he be of soul who could pass by
A sight so touching in its majesty:
This City now doth, like a garment, wear
The beauty of the morning; silent, bare,
Ships, towers, domes, theatres, and temples lie
Open unto the fields, and to the sky;
All bright and glittering in the smokeless air.
Never did sun more beautifully steep
In his first splendour, valley, rock, or hill;
Ne'er saw I, never felt, a calm so deep!
The river glideth at his own sweet will:
Dear God! the very houses seem asleep;
And all that mighty heart is lying still!

WILLIAM WORDSWORTH.

# Kew

Go down to Kew in lilac-time, in lilac-time, in lilac-time;
Go down to Kew in lilac-time (it isn't far from London!)
And you shall wander hand in hand with love in summer's
    wonderland;
Go down to Kew in lilac-time (it isn't far from London!)

The cherry trees are seas of bloom and soft perfume and
    sweet perfume,
The cherry trees are seas of bloom (and oh, so near to
    London!)
And there they say, when dawn is high and all the world's
    a blaze of sky
The cuckoo, though he's very shy, will sing a song for
    London.

The nightingale is rather rare and yet they say you'll hear
    him there
At Kew, at Kew, in lilac-time (and oh, so near to London!)
The linnet and the throstle, too, and after dark the long
    halloo
And golden-eyed *tu-whit*, *tu-whoo* of owls that ogle London.

For Noah hardly knew a bird of any kind that isn't heard
At Kew, at Kew in lilac-time (and oh, so near to London!)
And when the rose begins to pout and all the chestnut spires
    are out
You'll hear the rest without a doubt, all chorusing for
    London:—

*Come down to Kew in lilac-time, in lilac-time, in lilac-time;*
*Come down to Kew in lilac-time (it isn't far from London!)*
*And you shall wander hand in hand with love in summer's*
  *wonderland;*
*Come down to Kew in lilac-time (it isn't far from London!)*

ALFRED NOYES, from *The Barrel Organ*
(*Collected Poems*).

# York

IF you are interested in old things, in beautiful things, and in the history of this country, there is one city which will exceed your expectation—York.

I entered York with a mind full of misconceived ideas, and at this moment I feel (rather fatuously) that I have discovered York. I am thrilled to the spine to find not a great bustling capital of the north, but a peaceful, astonishingly beautiful medieval town, whose over-sailing houses are encircled by white, turreted city walls, which are a hundred times more interesting than the walls of Chester. York is too good to be true.

It is, to me, incredible, that a great city which marches through English history to the sound of trumpets and cathedral bells and the beating of drums should not have disfigured itself with gasworks and factories. York is the lovely queen—as London is the powerful king—of English cities.

Why did I expect York to out-Newcastle Newcastle?

In the south of England we suffer from a false idea of the manufacturing north. It is almost within the times of our grandfathers that the coalfields of the north became more important than the cornfields of the south, and we, having perhaps seen Sheffield from the train—one of England's saddest sights—imagine that a northern city must, in the nature of things, be an ugly one. The commercial prominence of those recent giants, Liverpool, Manchester, Leeds, Sheffield, Bradford, and Halifax, blinds us to the real north, which, apart from these areas of dense populations, remains, as it always has been, one of the most historically romantic and naturally beautiful divisions of England.

It is interesting to note that the industrial revolution has passed over such ancient aristocrats as Lancaster, Durham, and York. It is remarkable that Lancashire, which possesses Liverpool and Manchester, should own a delicious, sleepy old county town like Lancaster, and this in itself is symbolic of the fact that the great industrial new-rich cities of northern England—vast and mighty as they are—fall into perspective as mere black specks against the mighty background of history and the great green expanse of fine country which is the real North of England.

As for Yorkshire, it is not a county; it is a country; it is the grand old Northumbria of Saxon England! I could find enough in Yorkshire to keep my hasty pen busy day by day for a year, and that is why I must fly from it as I flew from Cornwall.

Leeds, Sheffield, and Bradford are three small circles in a land of abbeys, churches, castles, wild moorland, and heavenly dales, unchanged in parts since that time when the first monks went through Northumbria with the first crucifix.

I walked round the wall of York—which really looks like a town wall—rejoicing in this peerless city. York is not conscious of its beauty like so many ancient towns; it is too old and too wise and too proud to trick itself out for the admiration of tourists. That is one of the many reasons why I love it and its little country-town streets and its country-town hotels, called after the name of the proprietor. Here are no 'Majestics' or 'Excelsiors,' but plain 'Browns' and 'Joneses' and 'Robinsons.'

The street names of York are so eloquent that no words of mine can better describe the flavour of this ancient city. Listen to them: Gillygate, Fossgate, Shambles, Spurriergate, Goodramgate, Coppergate, Swinegate, Ogle Forth, Tanner's Moat, Palmers' Lane, Aldwark . . .

The streets of York have seen so much—no wonder they doze with half-shut eyes! They have seen the Roman lictors clear the way for Hadrian. Two Caesars died at York. It was here that the Emperor Severus came in A.D. 210 after his campaign in the north: a poor, broken, miserable master of the world, hiding his swollen limbs in a silk litter. Among his generals rode his own son, who was waiting for him to die. They said that birds of ill-omen cried on the gates of York when the Caesar passed in, broken in mind but not in spirit, for he is said to have quelled a mutiny from his litter. When the miserable mutineers knelt before him he raised himself on the cushion and, pointing to his swollen limbs, said: 'It is the head and not the feet which commands!' I would like to have heard the dying master of the world say that.

Trumpets blew and shields were beaten when Constantine the Great was proclaimed Emperor in York. How strange to think that Yorkshire sheep once gazed up from the grass to hear a great shout: 'Ave Caesar!' from the walls as another master took the purple and went on to his destiny.

H. V. MORTON, *In Search of England*.

# The Broads

MY own early memories are of the northern tributaries of the Bure, that drain the low-lying ground between the North Walsham to Bacton ridge and the coast. The easternmost part of the great joint estuary by Yarmouth is bare and bleak, and the upper reaches, near Wroxham itself and

Norwich, are too overgrown with trees. But the Ant, once you ascend to Stalham and Barton, seems to me to be blest both with something to look at and enough wind to send a boat along. Or it may be simply that I started there, in an open boat belonging to the redoubtable Dr Wheeler, my schoolmaster, pre-eminent in nearly every walk of life, certainly a great naturalist. To him, I owe (along with much else) early lessons at tugging at an oar (the boat took five of us for four days, its lockers were full, and it was no joke to pull). It was with him that I first penetrated into the maze of dykes and broads that lie between Stalham and the Bure, and up the Thurne, until I wondered why the few heaps of marrom-grass-grown sand prevented the fresh water from flowing out into the sea at Horsey Gap. Perhaps it did once reach the sea here, and may again. But it did not, that night in the 'nineties, when I, a little town-bred boy, helped to moor that open boat by the 'rond' of Waxham dyke, helped to adjust the mast longitudinally in its crotches, that fitted the gunwales, and spread over it the tarpaulin under which four of us were to sleep—one, I know, not without a feeling of awe. The marsh outside was so wide and lonely. As dusk descended on the smoky sunset, not a light —not a single friendly street lamp—was to be seen. Queer, unaccustomed sounds, with that of the neighbouring sea behind them all, began to overwhelm the stillness unbroken by human voice or footstep. We supped, and while some washed up, I accompanied the Doctor, armed with boat hook, ship's lantern, and net, to a yet lonelier place where, when the lighted lantern hoisted on the boat hook was thrust into the squelching uncertain ground, all kinds of queer moths came fluttering, and the Doctor skilfully caught them, examined, and either let them go (for his collection was already a large one), or put them in his bottle. Eventually he thought it was time for me to turn in with the others (he himself slept on the open 'Rond' wrapped in a blanket, under the stars, to give us more room in the boat.)

I well remember that journey, one of the most terrifying I ever took in my life, although but a few hundred yards, along the quaking uneven path, between high walls of reeds, amid the silence, or even more hair-raising, the queer life of the place, that seemed to hold its breath, and then scuttle or flap or swim away at my approach, circle round, and resume its slumber, or its uncanny nocturnal occupation, behind me. At last I saw before me the dull glow of the light, and heard the muffled voices of my companions, from beneath the tarpaulin. I remember, as if it were yesterday, the sensation of clambering aboard, the boat rocking slightly at its mooring, the unaccustomed look of those faces by candle-light, as they did odd jobs and prepared for rest. I saw nothing like it again until I entered a dug-out, twenty years later, and once more caught a glimpse of men huddled in that subfusc glow, gone primitive, to my town-bred notions. We laid ourselves down between the lockers and thwarts, adjusted our blankets about us on the hard foot-boards, and the night's rest began. Not immediately for me. The feeling of there being only an inch or so of board between me and the water, so friendly, light-reflecting and pleasant-sounding by day, so dark and sinister at night, was kept alive by the fact that whenever any of us moved, the boat balanced slightly, as some patient animal might beneath a redistributed weight. Then began a tiny scratching somewhere. Then a sudden scamper, a shriek of violence and terror, a splash, and some retreating noise I could not make out. I raised my head. 'Lie still, can't you!' came the voice of an older, country-bred companion, more used to this night life. He turned, muttering something about 'Vhoules!' which did nothing to quiet me, the word which did not then convey any animal shape, was too much like 'ghouls' or even 'souls.' I should not have been surprised in the least if the uneasy spirits of the queer breed of men had seen along the river banks that day, huge, weathered blue- or tawny-jerseyed people, in wherries, or doing queer

hings with nets and boats and even guns, were creeping
ilong the 'Rond' or rowing or wading round us, regarding
is as interlopers. The Doctor, of course, asleep beside the
reeds, I had heard him return some time after we laid our-
elves down, would fall an easy prey and we should be at the
nercy of the—er—natives, who might slit our throats and
:ut the boat adrift, and no one ever be the wiser, the current
vould carry it, a tarpaulined hearse, down the Thurne out
nto the Bure, perhaps right away across Breydon estuary
o the sea!

'Flap-lap-lap' went the water. Perhaps we were adrift
ilready! But no. I had seen and learned enough that day to
ecognize the slight outward movement of the bow, checked
is it met with the resistance of the mooring rope drawn taut.
We were still tied to the bank, though with enough slack to
illow for tide or other incident. How long I lay thus, just
)rave enough not to raise the alarm, I don't know, and have
10 doubt I dozed. The next thing I remember is the most
ieavenly music ever heard, lightest and most exquisite out-
)ouring of lovely sound. I sat up to see from whence it
:ould come and received a blow on the head that nearly
:oncluded my career on the spot. I did then open my eyes,
or I must have been dead asleep, and found I had hit myself
igainst the tiller. It was light. What a difference that
nade! Rubbing my head and creeping carefully along the
:hwart, though my companions were now all so dead asleep
is to render care unnecessary, I lifted the flap of the tar-
)aulin and looked out.

It was my first sight of dawn in the open country, and I
iave never forgotten it, and never quite recaptured the
:hrill. There was probably no house within a couple of
niles, and only one or two as near as that. But it might
iave been fifty miles. For all around on the tops of the
ushes lay a dense mist, faintly golden as the sun touched it,
ind right overhead, a dim blue. The effect can be seen in
Crome's picture 'Dawn,' which I always think should be

called 'Cockcrow.' Nowhere else that I know of has th
particular dew-and-mist-washed chill effulgence been ca
tured. Indeed, it can only be sought in the remotest Broa
land, or perhaps on the Suffolk Brecks. The sound th
had aroused me was of course the song of birds. Present
its lyric rapture was diversified by the queer metallic no
of snipe. Finally the Doctor stirred in his blankets, rous
us, and we rowed to the end of the dyke, tied up, and clai
bered over the sandhills to bathe in the icy sea (it was Wh
sun). Then back to breakfast, and never has banqu
seemed to me so delicious as those toasted sausages ai
coffee with condensed milk.

R. H. MOTTRAM, *East Anglia.*

# 6. Village Sketches

# A Yeoman

THIS man that at the wheatstack side
  Sits drinking of the twilight air,
This man's my friend, in him's my guide
  And guard against the traps of care.

His life now past meridian mark
  One can but say is blossoming yet,
His summer day smiles back the dark,
  His sun seems nearer rise than set.

In lusty youth when surging blood
  With foam and din bemuses most,
Leander-like he rode the flood,
  And strongly came to manhood's coast.

Since, with a sturdy steady tread,
  He sowed and stored himself good grain,
And glowing yet he bows his head
  With plough and scythe across the plain.

And like the north star stablished true
  He cheers and aids my asking eye;
To see him at his door anew
  Is like a sign shown in the sky.

With all his calm he's eager still,
  New dreams in his old vision thrive,
He seizes chance on dale and hill,
  And all his life has been alive.

EDMUND BLUNDEN. *English Poems.*

# Tom Cordery

THERE are certain things and persons that look as if they could never die: things of such vigour and hardiness that they seem constituted for an interminable duration, a sort of immortality. An old pollard-oak of my acquaintance used to give me this impression. Never was tree so gnarled, so knotted, so full of crooked life. Garlanded with ivy and woodbine, almost bending under the weight of its own rich leaves and acorns, tough, vigorous, lusty, concentrating as it were the very spirit of vitality into its own curtailed proportions—could that tree ever die? I have asked myself twenty times, as I stood looking on the deep water over which it hung, and in which it seemed to live again—would that strong dwarf ever fall? Alas! the question is answered. Walking by the spot to-day—this very day—there it lay prostrate; the ivy still clinging about it, the twigs swelling with sap, and putting forth already the early buds. There it lies, a type of sylvan instability, fallen like an emperor. Another piece of strong nature in a human form used to convey to me exactly the same feeling—and he is gone too! Tom Cordery is dead. The bell is tolling for him at this very moment. Tom Cordery dead! the words seem almost a contradiction. One is tempted to send for the sexton and the undertaker, to undig the grave, to force open the coffin-lid—there must be some mistake. But, alas! it is too true; the typhus fever, that axe which levels the strong as the weak, has hewed him down at a blow. Poor Tom Cordery!

This human oak grew on the wild north-of-Hampshire country, of which I have before made honourable mention; a country of heath, and hill, and forest, partly reclaimed, enclosed, and planted by some of the greater proprietors, but for the most part uncultivated and uncivilized; a proper refuge for wild animals of every species. Of these the most notable was my friend Tom Cordery, who presented in his own person no unfit emblem of the district in which he lived —the gentlest of savages, the wildest of civilized men. He was by calling rat-catcher, hare-finder, and broom-maker; a triad of trades which he had substituted for the one grand profession of poaching, which he followed in his younger days with unrivalled talent and success, and would, undoubtedly, have pursued till his death, had not the bursting of an overloaded gun unluckily shot off his left hand. As it was, he still contrived to mingle a little of his old unlawful occupation with his honest callings; was a reference of high authority amongst the young aspirants, an adviser of undoubted honour and secrecy—suspected, and more than suspected, as being one 'who, though he played no more, o'erlooked the cards.' Yet he kept to windward of the law, and indeed contrived to be on such terms of social and even friendly intercourse with the guardians of the game on M—— Common as may be said to prevail between reputed thieves and the myrmidons of justice in the neighbourhood of Bow Street. Indeed, his especial crony, the head keeper, used sometimes to hint, when Tom, elevated by ale, had provoked him by overcrowing, 'that a stump was no bad shield, and that to shoot off a hand and a bit of an arm for a blind would be nothing to so daring a chap as Tom Cordery.' This conjecture, never broached till the keeper was warm with wrath and liquor, and Tom fairly out of hearing, seemed always to me a little super-subtle; but it is certain that Tom's new professions did bear rather a suspicious analogy to the old, and the ferrets, and terriers, and mongrels by whom he was surrounded 'did really look, as the worthy keeper observed, 'fitter to find Christian hares and pheasants than rats and such vermin.' So in good truth did Tom himself. Never did any human being look more like that sort of sportsman commonly called a poacher. He was a tall, finely-built man, with a prodigious stride that cleared the ground like a horse, and a power of continuing his slow and steady speed that seemed nothing less than miraculous. Neither man, nor horse, nor dog could out-tire him. He had a bold, undaunted presence, and an evident strength and power of bone and muscle. You might see by looking at him that he did not know what fear meant. In his youth he had fought more battles than any man in the forest. He was as if born without nerves, totally insensible to the recoils and disgusts of humanity. I have known him take up a huge adder, cut off its head, and then deposit the living and writhing body in his brimless hat, and walk with it coiling and wreathing about his head, like another Medusa, till the sport of the day was over, and he carried it home to secure the fat. With all this iron stubbornness of nature, he was of a most mild and gentle demeanour, had a fine placidity of countenance, and a quick blue eye beaming with good humour. His face was sunburnt into one general pale vermilion hue that overspread all his features; his very hair was sunburnt too. His costume was generally a smock-frock of no doubtful complexion, dirt-coloured, which hung round him in tatters like fringe, rather augmenting than diminishing the freedom, and, if I may so say, the gallantry of his bearing. This frock was furnished with a huge inside pocket, in which to deposit the game killed by his patrons—for of his three employments, that which consisted of finding hares for the great farmers and small gentry, who were wont to course on the common, was by far the most profitable and most pleasing to him, and to them. Everybody liked Tom Cordery. He had himself an aptness to like, which is certain to be repaid in kind—the very dogs knew him, and loved him, and would beat for him almost as soon as for their master. Even May, the most sagacious of greyhounds, appreciated his talents, and would as soon listen to Tom sohoing as to old Tray giving tongue.

MARY RUSSELL MITFORD, *Our Village.*

# Mr Jagger

INDEED, if any urban alien has earned the right to naturalization in Monk's Norton it is Mr Jagger. He entered the village for the first time, by sheer accident, nearly thirty years before he settled in it. He came on a cushion-tyred bicycle, and dismounted for tea, with damson jam, at the 'Sheldon Arms,' then kept by Amos Perry, Fred Perry's father. It was on an April evening; then, too, a cuckoo had been calling from the elms in the field called The Cubbs at the back of the inn. Mr Jagger—a spry young business-man, with handsome moustaches, tight knickerbockers, and a pleated Norfolk jacket buttoned up to the level of an exceedingly high starched collar—had stepped out, after tea, into a world that seemed drenched with enchantment. Though the trees were but lightly fledged, the orchards stood dusted with plum blossom. The whole delicate scene was sketched in black and white with a wash of tenderest green that gave it an air of freshness and innocence, and the evening silence released such a torrent of birdsong as he had never heard before. Mr Jagger, refreshed and stimulated by his tea, left his bicycle at the inn door and explored the whole village on foot—from the white gate where straggling yew hedges concealed the Grange's gentility to the sandstone bridge, spanning the brook, over which he had arrived; from the watersplash, which complicated a cyclist's approach from the east, to the line of the 'cut' which was completely impassable. At the end of these explorations he visited the church. The porch gate was padlocked—it was unusual in those days for any one to enter the building except on Sundays—but the graveyard was full of old tombstones whose carven inscriptions were in tune with this bland, elegiac evening mood.

Idly scrutinizing these, with the mild sentimental detachment of a man in vigorous health and at peace with the world, he was brought up with a jolt by deciphering, on one of the oldest, his own name. 'Here lyes the body,' he read, 'of Ambrose Jagger, Farmer, of this Parish, 83 years of age.' The tombstone dated from the end of the eighteenth century: this Ambrose Jagger, he calculated, must have been born in the age of Queen Anne. From that moment his attitude, if still sentimental, was no longer detached. He sat there, in bemused reflection, till the flood of birdsong ebbed and the rooks came cawing home from their distant pastures. As he left the churchyard he felt at once awed and elated. He had a feeling that even if he had no part in those buried bones (and the coincidence of both names was remarkable) he had at least discovered a spiritual ancestor. He decided that if it were possible, he would certainly stay the night at the 'Sheldon Arms.'

It was possible, though somewhat unusual. Mr Perry confessed that he was not in the habit of catering for tourists. The visitor, in fact, was the first example of the species he had ever encountered: not unnaturally, since the road that entered Monk's Norton led nowhere in particular, and apart from a few of 'them there cyclists,' who poked in everywhere nowadays, strange faces were rarely seen.

That night Mr Jagger sat unobtrusively sipping sharp cider, which was treacherously potent, and listening to the slow talk of Mr Perry's customers in the bar. They were most of them older than himself, and, one and all, covered with a shaggy rustic patina, like lichen on weathered tree-trunks. The matter of their discourse was trivial, and their speech, at times, unintelligible; yet, in spite of these drawbacks, Mr Jagger experienced a burning though vain desire to be admitted to this exclusive society. The evening was well advanced before he plucked up courage to ask if any of his relatives, of the name of Jagger, remained in Monk's Norton.

'Jagger? Jagger?' the cronies repeated. They scratched

their heads and wagged them emphatically, deciding that nobody of that name or anything like it had ever been heard on there or thereabouts.

Mr Jagger enlightened them with enthusiastic details of the birth and death of his newly-acquired spiritual ancestor. Even these were received with caution. The sexton himself had never noticed the tombstone, though he was prepared, with polite reservations, to admit its existence.

'It's there all right,' Mr Jagger informed them proudly, 'and my name's Ambrose Jagger too.'

'If that's so,' the eldest of the party declared judicially, 'I reckon as this here gentleman has the right to count himself a Monk's Norton man.'

They laughed, dismissing the fantastic claim as a joke; but to Mr Jagger it was neither a joke nor fantastic. Up till then this timid and lonely little man had never experienced a sentimental attachment. From that moment his existence became dominated by one fierce desire: to enforce the shadowy claim and to identify himself with the past, the present, and such future as he might share with Monk's Norton. All his Hackney evenings were spent in bookish researches into its geography, geology, and history. So often as he could free himself from his clerkly employment —on every Bank Holiday and during his annual fortnight's vacation—he would push out his ancient bicycle and ride north-west into Worcestershire. In this manner he grew, by degrees, to be a familiar figure; a harbinger, like the cuckoos and swallows, of changing seasons. From 'that there cyclist chap' he became 'the gent from London,' and at last, 'Mr Jagger.' Eyes that had once regarded him with grudging surprise began to betray recognition and friendliness; nods welcomed him, and then smiles, and, finally, words.

'Well, well, sir, how be you? I was only a' saying to our Bob the other night: "It'll be just about time for Mr Jagger to be coming along again."'

Yet it was no less than fifteen years after he first set eyes on Ivy Cottage that Mr Jagger, arriving on his summer holiday, remarked the notice-board announcing that it was for sale. With this discovery a new and at first sight fantastic ambition entered his life. Up till now he had merely been possessed by the village: if he bought Ivy Cottage and the minute plot of ground on which it stood, he might count himself a possessor as well as possessed. No doubt the property would cost far more than he could command; yet the wild idea kept him awake as he tossed through that summer night in the trough of old Mr Perry's best feather-bed. Next morning he broached the subject timidly.

'Ivy Cottage? Ay, poor Mrs Tolley 's gone,' the landlord said, 'and her daughter-in-law, she wants to sell it, I 'm told. If so be as any one took a fancy to it, like, they might let it go for two or three hundred pounds. Mr Collins up at the Goodrest, he has the handling of it; but I 'm told Mr Sheldon-Smith has got his eye on it for the under-gardener.'

An anxiety akin to terror fell on Mr Jagger's mind. What, last night, had seemed a rash intoxicating aspiration, became an urgent desire. He bolted his breakfast, scalding his mouth with hot tea, and pedalled away with trembling legs through the watersplash to the Goodrest. The news that Mr Sheldon-Smith had his eye on the cottage dispelled his last shred of caution. He ran Mr Collins to earth looking over his lambs in the field called Long Dragon Piece. He panted:

'I 've come about Ivy Cottage.'

'What 's up? Not a fire?'

'No. I 've heard it 's for sale, and I want to buy it,' Mr Jagger said.

Mr Collins burst out laughing. 'If that 's all,' he said, 'you can have the place and welcome for two hundred and fifty . . . cash down, mind. It 's as good as a gift.'

Two hundred and fifty pounds. . . . It was approximately the total, at that moment, of Mr Jagger's savings, to the last penny he had scraped together during his working life. If he spent it, there would be nothing left between him and destitution, no line of retreat on which to fall back in case of disaster. The decision he made was, according to scale, heroic.

'Two hundred and fifty. Very well: I 'll take it,' he said.

Ivy Cottage is not, by Monk's Norton standards, beautiful. It was built in the eighteen-eighties, by the Sheldon-Smiths' predecessors at The Grange, in the very worst style of Victorian neo-gothic, with a high-pitched slate roof and small mullioned windows recklessly glazed with coloured glass. The parasite which gives it its name has mercifully obscured its architectural defects; and the style, after all, is in keeping with Mr Jagger's medieval mind. On his retirement he came to end his days in it. He is no longer the spry young commercial gentleman with the handsome moustache who 'discovered' Monk's Norton thirty years ago, though he still wears tight knickerbockers and a Norfolk jacket buttoned up to a high starched collar, and still rides a bicycle. He is, in fact, a rather seedy old man, with weak red-rimmed eyes and a wispy moustache. Yet his passion has never failed him. Monk's Norton, and everything that pertains to it—particularly to its past—remains the absorbing interest of his life. The subject, which he has made his own, is inexhaustible, and the carefully-docketed papers over which he broods for so many lamp-lit hours are concerned not merely with the place's documentary history, but with personal observations of such contemporary matters as records of rainfall and temperature and relative humidity; of the dates on which migrant birds arrive and are heard and depart and of their nesting habits; of the appearance of such rare and irregular visitants as crossbills and comma butterflies and (just once) a golden oriole. Since he came to live in Monk's Norton his range has widened. There is not a church within ten miles about which he does not know more than its incumbent. He writes letters to the local papers announcing the rarities he discovers, and correcting the loose conclusions of other local archaeologists. His life is completely solitary. How he contrives to exist on his minute savings remains a mystery. No doubt he receives a good many presents of perishable produce—an occasional basket of eggs or fruit, a sack of potatoes, or a barrel of cider—for most Monk's Norton people, though the village accepted him so tardily, are now proud of his erudition, and think of him as a 'character.' Others, including Major Sheldon-Smith, speak of him as a crank.

FRANCIS BRETT YOUNG, *Portrait of a Village.*

## The Blacksmith

I THINK the blacksmith is the most interesting man in our community. It so happens that our particular blacksmith, David Hookey, would be a most interesting man whatever his walk in life might be. I have never known a human being with so much quiet energy. In addition to his work as a blacksmith, he farms more than a hundred acres of arable land as well as pasture, on which he keeps a herd of cows. In these hard times for farmers he is compelled to do much of the work himself. He is the oldest member of our lifeboat crew, and has never once missed either a practice launch or a wreck; thus he has borne his part in saving more than one hundred and eighty lives. One would think it impossible for him to find time for anything else. But not so. He always has time to go fishing, and especially seine netting, whenever the sea is calm enough to enable us to indulge in that strenuous sport.

After ten hours at work on the farm and three hours in the forge, he gaily sets out at nine o'clock in the evening in his boat, with eighty fathoms of net piled up in the stern, to row round Brooke Point with me, to the long sandy beach two miles away. Arrived there, this indefatigable man will take charge of the proceedings, himself row the boat in the necessary wide sweep while the net pays out astern, then work harder than any one in hauling it in. Of course we are wet through all the time, but when the sport is ended at one or two o'clock in the morning, David thinks nothing of the labour of rowing the boat and the heavy net the two miles back round the outlying rocks of Brooke Point.

But the main thing is, for us who live here, that he provides that wonderful thing, the forge, just the same as it was a hundred years ago, now as then the most essential thing in the village, and, incidentally, the place of all others where one can best meet and talk of an evening. Of course there is the inn—that is a good place too; but one can go there if there is time after the visit to the forge.

When I get back tired and cold on an autumn or a winter's evening, it is good to be allowed to go to the forge. It provides life and warmth, from the friends one meets and from the smouldering fire which blazes up from time to time as the things we need are made out of pieces of iron, which our blacksmith chooses with unerring skill. There are the hearth, the bellows, the tank of cold water, the pieces of iron of all shapes and sizes, apparently in confusion, but to be found by the expert eye within two minutes, in the shape and form best suited to the purpose. It is all so old, and yet so modern in that it provides just what is wanted for us folk to-day.

Sometimes we offer to help with the bellows, but this art is such that at every critical moment it is only the blacksmith himself, or his trained assistant, who can provide the right amount of draught and heat. So those of us who are allowed to gather there mostly sit and watch, trying not to get in the way while these mysterious processes are gone through. Incredibly deft are the strokes of the hammer on the wellnigh molten metal, the result of forty years of experience and generations of inherited skill. Often it is horse-shoes to be made, for the brief post-war belief in a mechanical farm has died a swift death, as I knew it would. Again to-day, as formerly, twenty great horses pull the plough, and have to be shod. Hinges of gates, angle irons, a few modern things, such as elementary parts of tractors, have to be made, in just the same way as those which our blacksmith's grandfather was making when I was a boy fifty years ago.

So we sit there on a bench facing the glow, with the rain drying off our faces and our clothes, talking in whispers, until David Hookey has finished the job in hand. Then he must have a rest, for it is hard work swinging a great hammer for minutes on end without a moment's respite. The hot molten metal must be struck the shrewd hard blow just at the right time; the delicate operation of getting the shoe to take the exact curve in two dimensions must also be completed before the bar is cold. Then comes the driving of the nail-holes at the exact angle, so that the nail shall come out through the hoof far enough to give a good hold, but not so far as to risk pricking the foot—a triumph of human skill which filled me with wonder as a child, as it does to-day. Then the final operation—turning up the centre of the shoe, and the turning down of both ends in such a way that the grip of the shoe itself, in addition to the nails, shall be secured in the foot of the horse, which the blacksmith knows must rest on the ground in a way that suits that particular horse best. All these miracles of skill, for miracles they are, we sit and witness.

LORD MOTTISTONE, *For Ever England.*

# A Boy's Game

MORE than any other game, I take it, does a man play cricket consistently throughout his life, from infancy to mature age. He takes to golf, often enough, when youth is far behind, also to lawn tennis. He is almost born into cricket, and when he has become short in the wind and rather immovable in the flesh, he sits on the pavilion (or in the shilling seats) and plays the game by proxy, saying of Hobbs: 'There, but for the grace of the Lord, go I.' As a child he bowls underhanded grubs—even as in the early days of cricket they were bowled by the great old players. On the sands, by the seaside, every English boy has defended a wicket as primitive as the ancient hurdle—and has defended it with a bat not far removed from the curved weapon used in the distant past. To say the truth, most Englishmen live over again, as they play cricket, boy and man, for years, its technical history and development. The day a boy first attempts overhands is as epochal in his life as the day was in cricket's history when in 1807 John Willes bowled with his arm as high as his shoulder. When a boy can boast a control of the overarm ball the day is as important to him as the day on which he first wears long trousers—a day to be remembered throughout his longest years. He has now put childish (or girlish) things behind him; his sister cannot follow him into the great and true province of the game. Some modern girls no doubt can bowl overarms but the wonder is not that they do it badly but that they do it at all. And when the boy emerges to masterful youth and later to manhood, playing first for his school or village and then for his club or county, he has travelled himself along a hundred or more years of cricket's skilful course, from the misty and traditional origins to the complicated system which in our day has given us our splendid

and sophisticated masters. He may take his stand at the
wicket at Lord's and have his name pronounced by the
connoisseurs; he may bowl a Hobbs with one that goes up
the hill, but, whatever the conquest he achieves in his ripe-
ness, never will he forget the days when he was a boy: his
love for cricket blossomed then. The man who comes to
cricket after boyhood no doubt discovers many joys in the
game which hold him affectionately to it. But not for him
the felicity that visits those of us who see the coming of
every cricket season against a background of all the bygone
seasons of our schooldays.

And the boys who have the best of the fun are those so
poor that they have to begin at the very beginning, with
crude sticks and lumps of wood. There is an old print
which depicts a group of ragged boys tossing for innings in
a meadow. It is not a coin they have sent spinning into
the air but a war-worn cricket bat. If it falls down with
the hump of wood facing upwards, the lad who called
'Round!' will take the first knock. 'Round or Flat?' I
once asked Sir James Barrie if he ever tossed for innings in
this way. 'What *other* way is there?' he replied. Watch
any group of poor lads on a common playing cricket together and you are not far from cricket's first and eternally
flowing source, the fount of baptism now and always and
for ever.

I feel sorry for those cricketers who as boys have never
been so poor that they have had to go out into the fields
and find for themselves cricket's secret. The true heritage
of cricket is not something that can be bought by money;
a heritage is not exactly an heirloom. 'Round or Flat'—
do boys still toss for innings in this way? Or are they
nowadays so pampered that a penny piece (not to say a
sixpence) is always available; or is their cricket 'organized'
for them by grown-ups with a passion for Welfare? Once
on a time, boys who loved cricket used to 'club' together—
dear old phrase—for bats, balls, and wickets. There was

usually only one bat for the whole side—you dropped it when going for a run, so that the other boy batting with you could use it when he reached his 'end.' With only one bat in use, it came to possess, on certain occasions, a strange and mystical authority; in cases, for example, where there was argument as to whether a batsman was out or not. 'Don't give up your bat,' was the warning cry of his companions and allies. 'Don't give up your bat.' The law was not administered by umpires in *our* youthful matches; often a decision was put to a trial of strength. The bat was regarded as a symbol of office by the boy who happened to be holding it when the argument began. Perhaps there were no bails in use, and perhaps the contention was whether the ball had hit the wicket or not. 'You 're out!' 'No, I 'm not!' 'It 'it the middle stump!' 'No, it didn't!' It was at this point that we would put the dispute to the arbitrament of force. The attacking side descended on the batsman, and sought to sunder him from the bat. Once he had let go of it he was understood to have given up his last right to remain at the wicket—that mysterious and indefeasible right which is based upon possession. A cricket bat in our boyish eyes was more than an implement for the scoring of runs; it represented the game itself, the constitution and authority thereof. Its very age lent the aspect of sanctity; it was handed down from season to season; its many cracks and splits and bindings were like old runes and precedents, graven on a rod of law.

These boys play (yes, they still play, surely!) with a ball made of some hard, gritty material, held together by an adhesive substance which, in wet weather especially, renders the bowler very conscious of his office and function. It is called a 'composition' ball, and it is painted red, so that after a fellow has bowled with it a little while his hand is the dyer's, subdued to that it works in. This ball is perishable; it dwindles in circumference over by over—the batsman in last on his side gets rather less ball to hit at

than the batsman in first. Like many of the Hamble-
donians, again, we boys never wore pads. The lack of
them no doubt had certain shortcomings, but the leg-
before-wicket law was considerably simplified in conse-
quence.

Our wicket-keeper stopped the 'composition' ball not
with gloves or any other impedimenta excepting a coat
which usually was not his own. He would throw the coat
on the ball as it flashed past the stumps; a high degree of
dexterity was attained in the practice of throwing a coat
to a wide ball at the crucial moment. I have known many
byes to be run while the ball was being sought for, after it
had entered a secret place in the coat. I can see yet, with
my mind's eye, the stumper shaking the coat desperately
while the two batsmen scampered across the pitch. Yet
the cricket of these boys is not altogether crude. Blythe
was found in a rough field in Kent. And did not Hobbs
learn to bat with a lamp-post for wicket? The boys I have
in mind—where are they now?—used to read 'Badminton'
for hours and practise off-breaks. How they did spin on
the bare brown earth! We watched county matches at
Old Trafford, whenever there was a school holiday, or
whenever we plucked up courage enough to play truant.
Once I absented myself from school to watch R. H. Spooner
make a century—and he did. The night before I prayed
for it—'O Lord, let R. H. Spooner score 102 for Lancashire
against Yorkshire to-morrow, August 4th—for Lancashire,
O Lord.' It was a sunny day, and next morning my face
was as red as a beetroot. I was asked to explain my ab-
scence the previous day from school, and I said I had been
ill with scarlatina. I forget why I chose that particular
complaint as an excuse; I had no idea what it meant, and I
am afraid it proved unconvincing.

After we had watched our county darlings—Mold, Hirst,
'Ranji,' Jessop, Fry, Richardson—we would hurry home
from Old Trafford, and we would go out into the fields,

pitch our wickets, and play over again all the great deeds we had witnessed that day. One boy would strike a very elegant attitude at the crease and announce that he was Spooner. And he would be realist enough to cause a few hairs to stand up at the back of his head. Another boy would state that from to-night onwards he was putting slow bowling behind him. 'I'm Brearley,' he would say and begin to bowl as fast as his young limbs and heart would allow. A few weeks later the same boy (after the Lancashire and Yorkshire match) would very likely be seen bowling incredibly slow; he was now Wilfred Rhodes.

O the spaciousness of the August holidays in that far-off time. I see them now, lighted with sunshine in a world quiet and simple. There were fields to play cricket in near our great cities then. From morning till night we played, returning at noon for food and drink (ah, the ecstasy of cold water running from a tap!). Back we went to the dusty earth in the afternoon's heat; then a quick tea, and cricket again in the cool, slanting light of the evening. Our cricket, like that of all boys who ever lived or ever shall live, was quick with the spirit of hero-worship. We were in truth more like Maclaren and 'Ranji' than these men themselves, for we saw them ideally. Does the county cricketer always realize what he looks like in the eyes of a boy; what an obligation he is under not to let down and abuse young faith and vision? Not long since, I visited again the place where, years ago, we played our cricket and tossed for innings by shouting 'Round!' or 'Flat!' The fields are gone now; they are covered with rows of houses. At the fall of any lovely summer day, on the very spot where we as boys cut and drove and bowled, some house-wife stands at six o'clock and cooks a chop, while the evening sun shines through the scullery window.

If a moral has crept in hereabout it has done so behind our backs. None the less, we would do well to attend to it, unless we are hoodwinking ourselves when we think of

I

cricket as part of the English heritage.  Hobbs, no doubt, learned to play with a lamp-post in the street for wicket; Rhodes picked up his bowling in a country lane.  To-day a boy in either place playing bat and ball would stand a good chance of getting knocked to the earth.

NEVILLE CARDUS, Cricket.

## Sutton Club-Walking

THE old walls of the village pound are slowly crumbling. The holes between the stones offer a nesting-place to the tit. From the dusty mortar of the crevices grow spikes of pennywort a foot tall, and the yellow flowers of the stone-crop are bright in golden patches.  But although Sutton folk, on their way down the street, frequently stop in front of the pound, they take no note of such ordinary trifles as these. Their attention is always directed to the door.  It is a very old door with a small iron grating, at about the height of a man's eyes, through which people used to peep in search of stock that had wandered.  You can rarely see the grating now.  The bill-poster has made the door his own, and it is plastered half an inch thick.

The other afternoon, just as the stream of merry, noisy children came rushing out of school, the bill-sticker was pasting up another bill.  A crowd gathered round him at once, for elder people also came popping out of their houses.

'Read it out, one o' ee,' screamed the voice of Widow Teape.

One of the bigger boys began to shout: 'WHIT-MONDAY, JUNE 10, SUTTON FRIENDLY SOCIETY.'  But all the others took up the strain, until, presently, half the children of Sutton were reciting the contents of the poster, after the manner that you may overhear them through the open window, as you pass the schoolhouse, repeating poetry in class. And the purport was that Sutton Club would meet at 10; attend Divine service in the Parish Church at 11; dine in the marquee in a field kindly lent by William Purchase, Esq., at 1; that the sports would commence at 3; that the magnificent Oldbury Brass Band had been engaged, and that dancing would begin at 6.

From the time of this announcement until Whit-Monday a suppressed excitement was to be observed in Sutton Street. Out of all the rich succession of festivities that once made up the rural year, Sutton has retained only this one. But Sutton Club-Walking is celebrated, and there is no other for many a mile around. Cottagers from neighbouring villages flock to Sutton on Whit-Monday. Sutton knows that it has a reputation to keep up and does it.

Not but what there are croakers who try to find fault with the constitution of the club. They mutter that its economic system leaves a something to be desired, and predict its speedy decease. 'This 'll be the last,' they say. 'Village clubs can't stand up 'gainst the big societies. 'Tis the same wi' clubs as 'tis all the world over—the big do eat up the little.' Meanwhile the maidens get out their summer frocks, for the bill is out for this time, at any rate. They watch the opening rosebuds on the cottage front, to see whether any will be ready by the time, and 'worrit their heads' to find a new way of trimming up the house.

For the village is decorated at Club-Walking. Heppell lends scaffolding-poles, and at daybreak—because of Sunday it cannot be done overnight—his men are busy erecting a triumphal arch at the entrance to the field, where preparation has already been made for the marquee. At six the Union Jack flutters from the church tower and the bells strike out a peal. Before breakfast there is a festoon of flags from the upstair window of the smith's house to the sign of 'The Acorn.' Selina Jane Edwards has a string of bunting from the lilac bush to the clothes-pole on the other side of the path. The Widow Teape has fastened a Jubilee handkerchief, emblazoned with the Royal Arms, to a long lath, and her boy 'Urchett' has climbed up and lashed it to the top shoot of her apple tree. So the village is gay indeed. All being perfect, women in their best, maidens in their white, and children with great flowers in their buttonholes stand in their doorways, or by the garden hedges, or in groups upon the causeway, and adorn the street itself with palpitating human life. They are awaiting the arrival of the band.

The band is to be depended upon. Quite pat upon its hour it drives up in a brake and pair, with all the great brass instruments and the big drum in view. The children cheer, throw their hats into the air, and shout: 'Pla-a-ay up!' 'Pla-a-ay up!' But the band, conscious of fame, remains solemn. The drum sits self-contained. The trombone does not smile. Only a frivolous and romantic cornet has before now been known to wink at the village maidens as he passed. So it reaches its destination—the open space, which was once the village green.

At once all is stir.

The walkers are there, each bringing his pole with the brass head, a fleur-de-lis for Sutton, if he has one—for in a business age such trifles are no longer imperative. Old Abe, Japheth Pike, and some of the older men also wear scarves over their shoulders. Japheth Pike and young John Brook bring the great blue banner on two poles, bearing the legend in gold: 'Sutton Friendly Society.' The old rector in his surplice comes from the church and takes his position in front; the banner is raised; officials hurry members into rank; the band strikes up, and the club marches up the street, round the lane, and into the street again. In Sutton those who have no part in a procession never follow it. They are so eager that they run in front. But at the church the village stands on one side, and watches the club into the porch. Thus it has happened without change for many a year.

The old rector preached on this occasion on brotherly love. He could find no better subject, to be sure. The kindly parish was most lenient in its criticism of the sermon. But as Mrs Josiah Heppell afterwards said: 'Dear old man, to be sure! But la! what we do want is a young man up to the times, for a place like Sutton.'

The dinner was a hot dinner. It could not be otherwise under a marquee in June. Many of the ladies, wives and sweethearts of Sutton, were present. We dined off British beef, roast or boiled, or both. There was plum-pudding of a most admirable variety and a strong flavour of mixed spice. We drank good honest beer or cider, according to taste. We were hearty and merry, and laughed and joked, and at the end drank to 'The King' with a seemly reverence.

After that the serious business began, when we drank to 'Sutton Friendly Society,' associated with the names of Mr Richard Tucker, the treasurer, and 'Mr Ebenezer Dark, our worthy and energetic secretary.' For 'Uncle Dick' and 'Dairyman' are great supporters of the Club, and although paying members, would 'never dream of making claim either for sick- or walking-pay.'

We were ready for the sports and competitions; and the sheep-shearers, who do not require music, were started while the brass band, which had played during the speeches, retired into the marquee to dinner. Sutton was justly proud of the band, because ten years ago it gained a prize at a competition. It enjoyed eternal reputation on that great success. Uncle Dick in particular was anxious that the band should be kept well nourished and sustained, because much was expected of it, and the music was known to be first-class and remarkable. He walked from one to another, a jug in each hand, declaring that no man can blow brass if he's dry. Then came the sports, and in them we had no old-world games, no sack-races, no wheelbarrow, but a military tournament with tent-pegging and the slicing of lemons with cavalry swords. We did not really have lemons, which are expensive and scarcely known at Sutton, but substituted the finest potatoes eyes ever saw. The young yeomen of the surrounding district rode and slashed with such skill, that, as Uncle Dick said, half the parish might pick up a breakfast of teddies all chopped up an' ready to fry if they was a-minded.

Then there were pony-races and foot-races for girls, but still the thoughts of Uncle Dick, keeping always in view the evening dance, dwelt upon refreshment for the band. Now and then his voice might be heard across the field: 'For God's sake, Ebenezer Dark, don't let 's forget the band.'

The band was not forgotten. When the hour for dancing came there was a certain want of unanimity about the brass, but this was amply compensated for by the precision of the big drum. The youth of Sutton with peonies in their button-holes, without invitation, seized the willing maids all dressed in white and frisked and bobbed them round as merry as lambkins. You cannot waltz upon the grass, and they danced the old country dances of long ago which were so much like romps. At the winter dance in the schoolroom Sutton can waltz well enough and is proud of it; at Club-Walking they go back to 'Hunt the Squirrel' and 'Four-hand-reels.'

They were still at it as the dusk came creeping on. And still the voice of Uncle Dick was to be heard at intervals:

'Ebenezer, for God's sake, don't let 's forget the band.' I shall never forget the band.

WALTER RAYMOND, *English Country Life*.

# Miner

NEARLY every variety of industrial squalor can be studied in the neighbourhood of the Five Towns, where the private enterprise of the nineteenth century has turned a fair land into hell.

In one of the dreary townships of this district, which are strung together like black pearls on a string of motor-omnibuses, lives Bill, a Staffordshire miner.

Bill, like his Welsh confrère, is a straight-thinking fellow with a passion for all that is clean and decent and fair. You can see him sometimes on his off days, walking over the humpy country, a clay pipe in his mouth, a red muffler at his throat, and a whippet at his heels. You can see him also in the working-men's club, debating the ancient topic of Utopia with the ardour of a religious reformer.

His day begins at 5 a.m. While he puts on the garments that are dusty and polished with coal, his wife rises and, in the little kitchen-living-room downstairs, prepares his breakfast and what is known in Staffordshire as the 'snapping,' usually bread and margarine, or bread and cheese, which the miner takes with him to his work.

He kisses her good-bye—and the miner's parting from his wife every day is always, consciously or unconsciously, like that of a soldier going off to war—and, clattering in his clogs, awakening the echoes in the dark little street, he goes to the corner where the workmen's bus will come along with its yellow windows and its smell of men and tobacco. This is a luxury, and a welcome one. Bill's daily ride to the pit mops up two shillings from a meagre income, but it saves him a long and tedious tramp.

The pit-head and the mine chimneys loom up on a crest of ground, somehow rather fine and heroic in the pale light which is not yet strong enough to expose the shame of the broken earth, the squalor and the untidiness, the air of makeshift and the dirt. Bill gives in his check at the lamp room, is given a safety lamp, and is searched for matches. He then waits with the other members of his shift for the cage that will plunge them into the depths of the earth.

Mining was, is, and always will be, a horrible calling, and one that a stranger shrinks from as terrifying and unnatural. But just as generations of men make a fisherman, so generations of men who have striven below the ground make the modern miner. It is a calling that is born in a man; otherwise he could not endure it.

Therefore, with a casualness born of long experience, the men pack themselves into the wet and coal-grimed cage. The iron gates are shut, and the cage drops down, down, down into the earth. The walls of the shaft rush upwards, the air whistles past, and there is a bang and a rattle. The glow-worm lamps shine greenly in the cage, and the men look like souls consigned to hell.

Suddenly, the speed slackens; then the cage appears to hesitate slightly as it stops, with a surprising gentleness, at the pit-bottom.

Here is a still, hushed world. Bill does not think, as you and I would, of the millions of tons of rock and earth above him. His one thought is to be at the coal face, ready stripped to shovel coal on the conveyer sharp at 7 a.m.

He sets off along the dark tunnel, an ordeal so like trench warfare at night, so like a man moving up to the front line in the darkness. He passes the Onsetter, the autocrat of the pit-bottom.

The bright banter of the haulage boys comes to him in the darkness, making him smile—back-chat of the world above, chat about girls and cinemas and football. The boys dexterously hitch empty tubs to a rope, preparing the line of communication for the coal from the face to the pit-head. The bulky figure of the Road-doggie, the man in charge of these youths, looms up, hammer in hand and nails in pocket. His life is spent in rebuking the high spirits of youth and in nailing down the track. Then Bill tramps on in silence, coming at length to the coal face.

On the earth above and in the depths below, machinery has altered the life of man. Bill, although technically a miner, is actually a coal shoveller. The coal has been machine-cut and blasted. All the miners have to do is to shovel it like mad into a devouring monster known as the conveyer-belt. Seven and a half hours of constant coal shovelling, with a bare twenty minutes off for 'snapping' —that is the slavery of the modern machine face collier.

The conveyer-belt is a noisy, jigging trough that runs the length of the coal face. It can be fed at the rate of a ton a minute. The 'lobbers-on,' as the miners are called, look like stokers shovelling for dear life.

The appearance of slavery is made perfect by the system under which Bill shovels coal. It is known politely as the contractor system, but among Bill and his friends it is still called by the old-fashioned name—the 'Butty System.' Some students of industrial problems will tell you that the 'Butty System' was abolished long ago. But this is not so. It still exists where it originated, in the Midlands; and its history is interesting.

In the early nineteenth century the large coalfields, the property of wealthy landowners, were worked on the feudal system, but the smaller mines of Derbyshire and Staffordshire were sometimes leased to contractors—who were often publicans—known as 'butties.'

This system had all the evils and horrors of slavery, for the 'butty' was often both a bully and a blood-sucker.

In the afternoon the cage takes Bill up to the welcome light. He fills his lungs with the clean air and enjoys the first sudden glimpse of sunlight.

Bill's opinions on life? Here they are:

'The most wonderful thing about the miner is his wife. She is the magician who makes ends meet. Only God knows how.

'There are more Black Fridays than Good Fridays with the miner's pay envelope, and, roughly, we average about £2 a week, taking the good with the bad.

'Out of that we must pay Union, bus fare, and sometimes a levy if we break a lamp glass or a tool. A good week means butter; a bad week means margarine.

'The miner is a cheerful bloke: so was the Tommy in the trenches. Our work demands co-operation, which always brings out the best in men. It's also the kind of work that makes a man love his home.

'As far as this work goes, my belief is that far too much blood has been spilt at the call of private profit. I, and many another miner, believe that ninety per cent of mine accidents could be avoided if the mines were State-owned.

'I believe that all shot-firing in mines should be abolished, because it only takes one shot to make a tragic newspaper headline.

'I think working hours should be reduced, so that some of our unemployed brothers could be brought in, and I think that minimum wages should be £3 a week, not to mention full pay when on the injured list. . . .'

Such are the words of Bill.

H. V. MORTON, *Our Fellow Men.*

# Pre-war Country

THE fact cannot be avoided: how much that we loved is going or gone! It is not a tremendous old age that has justified me in this exclamation. I am still merely an old young man. I have known an England in which the water-mill and the windmill were regular, familiar workers; and

already the few of them that have not been dismantled by weather or by the improver are anxiously numbered up as antiquities which ought, if we can contrive it, to be preserved. It is a great rarity to find one that is still working —sometimes they suffer the indignity of being used as sheds for oil engines. The streams of my old home were kept clear and lively by a system of sluice-gates and tumbling-bays, when farmers flourished who understood the matter; those streams are now choked and stagnant. Ponds, that were felt to be valuable for just their beauty, are rubbish heaps; the owners have no eye for them. Rivers that poured a pure wave are defiled with the poisons that accompany our mechanical development; the radiant noonday pool in which you saw here a shoal of bluish bream, there a hundred silvery roach, and a pike or two on the warm sandy shallow beyond, is not to be seen. Paths that were as good as roads are overwhelmed with nettles and briars; or the stiles that admitted to them are uprooted, and wire fences run in their stead; although we never needed our paths so manifestly. Meadow after meadow disappears; the rabbit scarcely has time to move out before the new row of villas is affronting the retreating woods with the confectionery of the builder's yard.

But I did not mean to be indignant—elegiac only, or perhaps a trifle boastful. It is something to have lived out of one epoch into another. I lived in the epoch of the horse, and went to school on a winter morning often riding on the tailboard of the long wagon loaded with apples, drawn by a team of horses—a magnificent picture, which has ceased to appear. The natty red mail-van no longer goes gliding by; the carrier's hooded wagon is forgotten; the baker no longer makes his tour from dawn till dark behind his pony; our cricketers do not order the horsed brake for their matches in villages over the hill. And with them you can see a particular effect: whereas in the old days of the brake they went out together and so returned, in the moments of the motorcycle they hurl themselves separately at their destinations. The loss is not only one of a picturesque spectacle, but of a social idea.

It might be almost as difficult to put up a horse now at many wayside inns as it would have been twenty years ago to buy petrol there.

I have been one of the latest witnesses of the old kind of threshing-floor, and the skill of the thumping flail; of the sickle cutting through acre after acre, of the gleaners following at their understood distance. On Sussex Downs, I once saw the oxen dragging the wooden ploughs. Almost as far away seem the processions of people to church and chapel on Sundays.

Black hoods and scarlet crossing hill and dale.

Among them, in my parish, were the boys of the little endowed school, with their tasselled caps and wide collars, conducted along by the last of the Ushers. In winter, I have been among the drove of young men and boys who went out in the moonshine to slide and caper over the frozen meadow lakes—a simple pastime. 'Big Man Slide,' 'Little Man Slide'—the terms are surrounded with merriment beneath a sky of terror and glory; we went forth with natural impulse, a community. I knew my village as one of great trees, and hidden beauties; the trees are mainly felled from one cause and another, there are not many surprises in the emphasized plan of roads, houses, and fences. The sweet-shops that I remember were usually indicated by nothing more than a box or two of popcorn and 'home-mades' in the front window of a cottage; those were for us who had time to stop and stare; to capture attention now-adays Mrs Giles must set up a battery of posters and pictures. The inns were humble, semi-private places; they too must now bedizen themselves with proprietary labels, loud, often nearly meaningless. Thus, the windows of 'The Bull' will be found plastered with the goggling trademark of a hippopotamus or so, in dismal repetition, who has nothing to tell me, though repeated to the nine hundred and ninety-ninth time, about the cardinal points of old ale, a bite of bread and cheese, and a landlord who makes one welcome.

The aeroplanes that gloriously fly over us do not make the small boys put down their bats and balls; but after all they are here and over the hill in almost less time than the writing of these words requires.   I was a cricketer of the same stamp in the balloon age, and a balloon gives you some chance.   I see a red balloon still, bowing and turning along above us; and I see Miss K. running out to take us to the hilltop for as long and near a sight of this magic vessel as could be had. Coming down!   That ultimate pleasure of approaching the vision, it is true, was not granted.

The wooden bridges which used to shake ominously under the passage of our wheels were replaced soon after I had formed my dreams upon them and the deeps below.   They carried roads of no small importance.   Their steepness tested the judgment of carters and the muscles of horses; life is certainly easier that way.   I knew the village pound on the common, where the boys watched their cows, although it was never used in my day for the stray animal and the reward of the finder; but now the children do not know that the square palings are a pound, or what, other than money, that word can mean.   They have scarcely any notion, moreover, of the joys of the blacksmith's anvil and musical pyrotech-nics—it was worth taking a hoop to him for repair as an excuse for loitering and admiring the red glare and the giant energies for shoeing mighty dray horses.   And every day almost was the forge's day.

Even at the railway station the last age had something of its own.   The stationmaster's beard and top hat have gone with it.   The bell no longer rings in his ceremonious hand before the trains come.   The trains are not so im-portant—they are not now what they were, the only loco-motive fashioners of our lives except in our own little sphere, the messengers and agencies from and to London and the wide world. What crises, what fortunes, depended on their fiery banners on the cloud of night, their grand lowings and throbbings and hissings! They are, in a mechanical inquiry, as they then were; but their impact on one's attention and imagination is fallen away.

But my catalogue must be broken off, for in England you can never be sure that the thing you missed will not meet you round the next turn of the lane—and who, at least among those whose days are cabined, cribbed, confined by the demon Work, can speak of England except in such a parochial manner as I have been doing?

EDMUND BLUNDEN, *The Face of England*.

## The Carrier

IN the early hours of morning, Ephraim, the Carrier, became vaguely conscious of the dawn of another day. There was no light in the little bedroom, but some instinct told him that the clock in the tower of the village church would soon confirm his belief. This it did forthwith on five sonorous strokes. 'Up, flesh, up!' cried Ephraim to Ephraim, and, as though in order that the summons should not be disregarded, jumped out of bed. Before assuming waistcoat, coat, or neckerchief, he tramped downstairs, lit the kitchen fire, put on the kettle, and then proceeded to the stable, where he groomed and fed Ebenezer, the two-and-twenty year old cart-horse that carries him from village to village. This work done, he went to the scullery for some soap and walked to the pump for the morning wash. Breakfast followed, tea, bread and butter, a small piece of cold bacon, and a long hearty grace, after which Ephraim started to load the big cart. He carried one barrel and three or four five-gallon drums of paraffin, one of which had leaked badly into the yard, and required attention and replenishment.

Then there were half a dozen small sacks of coal, a case of oranges, and one of apples, several packets of matches, wick, and burners for oil lamps, and some other odds and ends, bootlaces, packets of cocoa, sweets, soda, and soap. All these goods required careful packing behind his end of the cart in order that room might be available for stray passengers, and by the time all was in order, Ebenezer harnessed, and the cottage locked up, the clock was striking seven. It was a sharp January morning. The frost had been in charge all night, and now the sun would soon resume control; the wind was in the east.

'Please, Efrum, gi 'e us a ride to school.' This was the cry that assailed him about an hour later when he was among the cottages on the Maychester marshes, and, as he never refused a request, he soon had half a dozen boys and girls chatting with him merrily. Then came two paying passengers, a widow and daughter bound for a point at which they might catch the two-horse 'bus that travels once a week to Market Waldron in time for the morning train.

'Ebenezer can't do no more than jub along, my dear,' remarked Ephraim to the widow, 'but he 'll git ye there. Come now, Ebenezer,' and lifting his stick he directed a heavy blow at the rail over which the reins pass. Ebenezer, though knowing that no blow comes nearer than the rail, responded with a slight flick of the tail and raised his pace to four miles an hour.

'You don't wanter press th' hoss, Efrum,' remarked the widow.

'There 's many a time I bin and towd Ebenezer that 's lucky I 'm same as a patient man,' remarked the Carrier. 'Didn't, I 'd ha' had a moty car that 's likely. But there, th' good Lord bin and spared me, so I count I gotter spare Ebenezer.'

'Lor', Efrum, you don't wanter talk about gettin' a moty

car,' said the widow. 'Did, I ouldn't ride along o' you. Nasty dangerous things to my thinkin'. Git over me people go inter 'em. I never bin in one.' When they had left him and the children had been set down near the school-house, Ephraim proceeded to three remote villages in turn, and found his customers waiting with a welcome. He works on a minimum of profit; he has never been known in all his life to tell a lie, and, as an Elder of the Peculiar People, enjoys all the respect he has earned in a district where Non-conformity is the dominant form of belief. His competitors from distant villages, though some are equipped with motor vans, have long decided to leave his parishes alone.

About midday Ebenezer was released from bondage and received in the stables of an offhand farm, where the labourer who lives in the remains of the farmhouse insisted upon unharnessing him and quietly added a handful of his master's good, sweet hay to the meal that a well-filled nose-bag held. Ephraim produced his own bread and cheese, the labourer's wife provided a cup of tea, and her husband a fine onion, and the carrier acknowledged their kindness first by giving an orange to each of the children, and then, the simple meal finished, offering up thanks.

More work followed, and, with a greatly diminished load, tired horse and tired man turned upon the homeward way, rather behind their usual time. Evening was falling. As the old cart creaked along the lane leading into Maychester a man knocked at the door of the Carrier's cottage. Hearing no movement he walked to the stable, and, finding that closed, lit his pipe and threw the lighted match on to the ground. He did not see, as he passed out, how the wisps of hay caught fire and the fire spread to the tar-coated stab-ling. He was not to know that the match had fallen where the paraffin that leaked from the drum had soaked the ground. A great cloud of smoke, stabbed by flame, greeted the Carrier as he approached his home. . . .

Maychester came readily to the rescue. Men and women

lined up from the village pump to the cottage and passed buckets along, and a car sped to the nearest telephone to summon the engine from Market Waldron; but the wind was strong, house and buildings were alike inflammable, and the most that could be done was to keep the flames from spreading. The old man worked in line with the rest, saying no word as his home surrendered to the fire. Only when all that could be done had failed he went to each helper in turn, and said: 'Thanky, friend.'

'You must come to mine, Efrum,' cried a neighbour, 'f'r a bite an' a bed.'

'I couldn't eat, friend,' replied the Carrier, 'an' I count I 'll lay in th' chapel to be near th' Lord in me tribbylation. But if you 'll take pore Ebenezer an' look arter he, I 'll thank ye kindly. He 'll be downright reg'lar hungry.'

S. L. Bensusan, *Village Idylls.*


# For J. P.

It was in pleasant Derbyshire
  .Upon a bright spring day,
From a valley to a valley
  I sought to find a way;
And I met a little lad,
  A lad both blithe and bold;
And his eyes were of the blue,
  And his hair was of the gold.
'Ho! little lad, of yonder point
  The name come quickly tell!'
Then, prompt as any echo,
  Came the answer:—'Tap o' th' hill.'
'But has it any other name
  That a man may say—as thus—

k

*Kinderscout*, or *Fairbrook Naze*?'
　　Then said the child, with constant gaze:—
'*Tap o' th' hill* it gets with us.'

'Yes, yes!' I said, 'but has it not
　　Some other name as well?
Its own you know?' 'Aye, aye!' he said,
　　'Tap o' th' hill! tap o' th' hill!'
'But your father, now?　How calls it he?'
　　Then clear as is a bell
Rang out the merry laugh:—'Of course,
　　He calls it Tap o' th' hill!'
So I saw it was no use;
　　But I said within myself:—
'He has a wholesome doctrine,
　　This cheerful little elf.'
And O, the weary knowledge!
　　And O, the hearts that swell!
And O, the blessed limit—
　　'Tap o' th' hill! tap o' th' hill!'

　　　　　　　　T. E. BROWN, *Collected Poems.*

# 7. The Vandals

# Picking Flowers

THE plain fact of the situation is that, if human beings go on picking flowers as greedily as they do at present, there will soon be few flowers left in the country to pick. There is precisely the same argument for forbidding people to pick flowers—or, at least, for forbidding them to pick flowers by the basketful or to dig them up by the roots—as there is for forbidding people to cut the pictures in the National Gallery out of their frames and to take them home with them. Any one with a sense of beauty must occasionally have longed to carry off a picture from a public gallery. What beauty it would lend to the home! How much lovelier it would seem there than on the dull walls of a crowded gallery! There is only one argument against taking it—that there are not enough good pictures to go round. And we have now reached a stage at which there are not enough wild flowers to go round. In the old days a meadow of wild daffodils was lavish beyond the needs of a countryside. With the popularization of the bicycle, however, began the invasion of the country by the hordes of the town, and no sooner were the daffodils in flower than long processions of cyclists bore down on them and went home with the blooms as trophies on their handle-bars. And, now that the motor-car has been added to the bicycle, the pillage of the fields is increasing tenfold. Roots are dug up and carried off to add to the amenities of a suburban garden. Primroses and blue-bells are torn from the wayside to die on a drawing-room table. It is a charming instinct that impels human beings to do these things—the same instinct that once led them to shoot and stuff dead birds and to hang dead butterflies in glass cases on their walls. And it was an instinct with which it was difficult to quarrel so long as the riches of nature more than kept pace with the amiable greed of mankind. But nature is announcing the possibility of exhaustion. Birds and butterflies have disappeared within the memory of men still living, and forest glades which old men remember as gardens in June are now as flowerless as the Strand.

Thus, there is good reason for considering the lilies of the field in a different fashion from our grandfathers. We must cease to behave as our grandfathers behaved in order to preserve the world that our grandfathers knew. It is pleasant enough to burlesque the notion of a policeman haling a child before the magistrate for making a daisy-chain; but we know that in practice that is not the sort of thing that is going to happen, and that laws can be made that will leave abundant flowers in the country places without branding children who pluck a wild rose as criminals. Last year, the Hertfordshire County Council passed a by-law which prohibited the uprooting of wild flowers and ferns in the county; and Londoners who visit Hertfordshire in their cars during the weekend will enjoy the countryside no less on that account. I know fields that were once banks of flowers that are now wildernesses as a result of the mania for uprooting. It is easy to see that, if the mania increased sufficiently, the Home Counties would in time become as bare of many of the most beautiful flowers as Hampstead Heath. The locust is not more destructive than the lover of flowers who kills and steals the thing he loves. He is as much an enemy of the pleasures of other men as a man who would shoot nightingales.

Common sense suggests, indeed, that we should be at as much pains to preserve the flowers of the countryside as to preserve historic buildings or birds or big game. I am not sure that it would be a bad thing to forbid the sale of wild flowers, for the increasing sale of wild flowers has undoubtedly helped to diminish and destroy them. There are enough flowers grown in gardens to fill all the bowls and vases in the towns, and there is no need to raid the fields for

[CORNISH DAFFODILS

such purposes. If we wish to preserve the country we shall have to begin to look on the birds and flowers that populate it as we look on the birds and flowers in a park. They are there for our pleasure, not for our appropriation. The country is no longer a wild place of unlimited exuberance. It is a nation-wide garden. Not that it need ever become tame like a garden. In a sane world, we shall never have to breed goldfinches deliberately as we breed hens, and campion and rest-harrow, unlike tulips, will grow uninvited. The country will remain as it always was if only we leave it alone. Even a London building plot fenced-in returns in a few months to the riches of nature. The country can be most easily saved, indeed, not by doing something about it, but by doing nothing about it—not even uprooting a fern. It is the simplest recipe for the creation of a beautiful world that was ever invented. Leave it alone, and you will have butterfly orchises and all the other toys of nature in abundance. Nature is no niggard, but even nature demands a rest from the restless voracity of man. She will become a spendthrift only if we become careful. Only if we grow civilized will she remain wild.

ROBERT LYND, *It's a Fine World.*


# The Curse of Litter

It was one of the most beautiful districts in the West of England; the weather was glorious, and the meridian sun smote hotly down upon hill, valley, and ocean. Shelter on that particular eminence seemed scarce; but here at last was a comfortable stone boundary fence overhung with young beeches and other cooling foliage, and inviting instant repose. A pipe, and all would be perfect; but careful search produced not a single match. Was any one likely to pass by with one? The chances, on that height, seemed adverse.

But the *deus ex machina* actually arrived: a tall, spare, grizzled man, evidently accustomed to much tramping. The need being suggested, he opened a satchel which he carried, and proffered not a match but an entire new box, and in so doing showed that the satchel contained not one box, but many, perhaps half a gross.

No, he said, as if anticipating a question which courtesy refrained from putting; no, he did not travel in matches, or if he did, it was only in the sense used by the bridegroom who explained that he travelled in confetti, when he came to undo his overcoat at the hotel. If he travelled in matches it was for no commercial purpose; his object was philanthropic, aesthetic. And he heaved a sigh, and mopped his brow.

Confidence having been established, he began to speak of the hardships of his self-imposed lot; for self-imposed it was, and he never expected to obtain any thanks or recognition for it. Daily he trudged, on an average, at least twenty miles, and a single box of matches went no distance; he could not say how many would be wanted in August when the holiday people would be ubiquitous; the work was quite bad enough now, and later on he feared he might succumb to it. To a certain extent the fine weather was responsible, for it brought the trippers, the picnickers, and the ramblers generally out; on the other hand wet weather, if it kept the multitudes down, prevented him from accomplishing his task. But then again, if it was impossible on wet days, it had to be done with much more care in periods of drought, for grass, gorse, and heather then became like tinder, and he had to see that his fires did no damage.

A superb part of England, this—he went on, but utterly changed since he was a boy. This was his third season, so to speak; three years ago he had retired from London and crowds and noise, and had come with the brightest anticipations of finding peace and nature unsullied in the West of his upbringing. At that moment he interrupted his discourse, darted forward into a patch of bracken, hooked out upon the pathway with his stick a dirty old newspaper, put a match to it, and saw that it burnt itself out.

That was his job, he explained, his business in life now, if we had not already guessed it. Burning up the accursed, disfiguring, disgusting remains of other people; complete and total savages, whatever their social status, their means, their education, their personal and domestic habits. It was extraordinary how quite decent persons, who would tolerate nothing unclean or slovenly at home, forgot themselves on an outing in the country. They threw away their paper without a thought for the pleasure of others; the more a place was esteemed as a 'beauty-spot' the worse they befouled it. Local people, he added, were every bit as bad as casual strangers. Look at L——, for instance: ruined by old newspapers, old bags, old chocolate wrappings, old cigarette cases; one knew the different colours of the various brands, and cursed the manufacturers' sense of prettiness. Look at C——, where there was a precipice of unsurpassed natural beauty, and hundreds daily came to see the view from it, and faithfully shot their refuse down the slope. In these days of universal trippers, and country holidays, and half-holidays for all, the best parts of England would soon be submerged in litter; but nobody seemed to mind. He would like to see offenders fined pretty heavily, but the expense of detection would be enormous.

So he did what he could, in his own dearest *angulus terrarum*; but he knew it was sheer quixotry. Fire, too, was a dangerous element; and few, especially in this weather, could be relied upon to consume their leavings without blackening a hillside, either by accident or on purpose. The present year would be critical for him; unless local authorities woke up to defend the scenery which brought money into their district, no one with an eye for nature could stay in the country. He thought next year he would probably be moving back to London.

But he must say good-day; he knew of a place whitening with his own peculiar harvest, and he felt bound to make for it without wasting more time. *Pagina ne nimium crescat* were his last overheard words, before he pounced upon another provocation.

EDWARD GREY, *The Open-Air Year*.

# Abuse of the Countryside

THE road mounts the low Downs again. The boundless stubble is streaked by long bands of purple-brown, the work of seven ploughs to which the teams and their carters, riding or walking, are now slowly descending by different ways over the slopes and jingling in the rain. Above is a Druid moor bounded by beech-clumps, and crossed by old sunken ways and broad grassy tracks. It is a land of moles and sheep. At the end of a shattered line of firs a shepherd leans, bunched under his cape of sacking, to watch his black-faced flock dull-tinkling in the short furze and among the tumuli under the constant white rain. Those old roads, being over hilly and open land, are as they were before the making of modern roads, and little changed from what they were before the Roman. But it is a pity to see some of the old roads that have been left to the sole protection of the little gods. One man is stronger than they, as may be known by any one who has seen the bones, crockery, tin, and paper thrown by Shere and Cocking into the old roads near-by as into a dust-bin; or seen the gashes in the young trees planted down Gorst Road, Wandsworth Common; or the saucy 'Private' at the entrance to a lane worn by a hundred generations through the sand a little north of Petersfield; or the barbed wire fastened into the living trees alongside the footpath over a neighbouring hill that has lately been sold. What is the value of every one's right to use a footpath if a single anti-

social exclusive landowning citizen has the right to make it intolerable except to such as consider it a place only for the soles of the feet? The builder of a house acquires the right to admit the sunlight through his window. Cannot the users of a footpath acquire a right, during the course of half a dozen dynasties or less, to the sight of the trees and the sky which that footpath gives them in its own separate way? At least I hope that footpaths will soon cease to be defined as a line—length without breadth—connecting one point with another. In days when they are used as much for the sake of the scenes historic or beautiful through which they pass as of the villages or houses on this hand or that, something more than the mere right to tread upon a certain ribbon of grass or mud will have to be preserved if the preservation is to be of much use, and the right of way must become the right of view and of very ancient lights as well. By enforcing these rights some of the mountains of the land might even yet be saved, as Mr Henry S. Salt wishes to save them. In the meantime it is to be hoped that his criticisms will not be ignored by the tourists who leave the Needle Gully a cascade of luncheon wrappings and the like; for it is not from a body of men capable of such manners that a really effective appeal against the sacrifice of 'our mountains' to commercial and other selfishness is like to spring.

And those lone wayside greens, no man's gardens, measuring a few feet wide but many miles in length—why should they be used either as receptacles for the dust of motor cars or as additions to the property of the landowner who happens to be renewing his fence? They used to be as beautiful and cool and fresh as rivers, these green sisters of the white roads—illuminated borders of many a weary tale. But now, lest there should be no room for the dust, they are turning away from them the gipsies who used to camp there for a night. The indolent District Council that is anxious to get rid of its difficulties—for the moment—at the expense of a neighbouring district—it cares not—will send out its policeman to drive away the weary horses and sleeping children from the acre of common land which had hitherto been sacred—to what?—to an altar, a statue, a fountain, a seat?—No! to a stately notice-board; half a century ago the common of which this is a useless patch passed on easy terms to the pheasant lords.   The gipsies have to go.   Give them a pitch for the night and you are regarded as an enemy of the community or perhaps even as a Socialist.   The gipsies shall be driven from parish to parish, and finally settle down as squalid degenerate nomads in a town where they lose what beauty and courage they had, in adding to the difficulties of another council.   Yet if they were in a cage or a compound which it cost money to see, hundreds would pay for a stare at their brown faces and bright eyes, their hooped tents, their horses, their carelessness of the crowd, and in a few years an imitation of these things will be applauded in a 'pageant' of the town which has destroyed the reality.

EDWARD THOMAS, *The South Country*.

# 8. Nostalgia

# Home Thoughts from Abroad

OH, to be in England
Now that April's there,
And whoever wakes in England
Sees, some morning, unaware,
That the lowest boughs and the brush-wood sheaf
Round the elm-tree bole are in tiny leaf,
While the chaffinch sings on the orchard bough
In England—now!

And after April, when May follows,
And the whitethroat builds, and all the swallows—
Hark! where my blossomed pear-tree in the hedge
Leans to the field and scatters on the clover
Blossoms and dewdrops—at the bent-spray's edge—
That's the wise thrush; he sings each song twice over,
Lest you should think he never could recapture
The first fine careless rapture!
And though the fields look rough with hoary dew,
All will be gay when noontide wakes anew
The buttercups, the little children's dower,
—Far brighter than this gaudy melon-flower!

ROBERT BROWNING.

## The Reverie of Poor Susan

AT the corner of Wood Street, when daylight appears,
Hangs a Thrush that sings loud, it has sung for three years:
Poor Susan has passed by the spot, and has heard
In the silence of morning the song of the Bird.

'Tis a note of enchantment; what ails her?  She sees
A mountain ascending, a vision of trees;
Bright volumes of vapour through Lothbury glide,
And a river flows on through the vale of Cheapside.

Green pastures she views in the midst of the dale,
Down which she so often has tripped with her pail;
And a single small cottage, a nest like a dove's,
The one only dwelling on earth that she loves.

She looks, and her heart is in heaven: but they fade,
The mist and the river, the hill and the shade:
The stream will not flow, and the hill will not rise,
And the colours have all passed away from her eyes!

WILLIAM WORDSWORTH.

## At the Wars

Now that I am ta'en away,
And may not see another day,
What is it to my eye appears?
What sound rings in my stricken ears?
Not even the voice of any friend
Or eyes beloved-world-without-end,

['A MOUNTAIN ASCENDING, A VISION OF TREES'

But scenes and sounds of the countryside
In far England across the tide:
An upland field when Spring's begun,
Mellow beneath the evening sun. . . .
A circle of loose and lichened wall
Over which seven red pines fall. . . .
An orchard of wizen blossoming trees
Wherein the nesting chaffinches
Begin again the self-same song
All the late April day-time long. . . .
Paths that lead a shelving course
Between the chalk scarp and the gorse
By English downs; and, O! too well
I hear the hidden, clanking bell
Of wandering sheep. . . . I see the brown
Twilight of the huge empty down. . . .
Soon blotted out! for now a lane
Glitters with warmth of May-time rain,
And on a shooting briar I see
A yellow bird who sings to me.

O yellow-hammer, once I heard
Thy yaffle when no other bird
Could to my sunk heart comfort bring;
But now I would not have thee sing,
So sharp thy note is with the pain
Of England I may not see again!
Yet sing thy song: there answereth
Deep in me a voice which saith:
   '*The gorse upon the twilit down,*
   *The English loam so sunset brown,*
   *The bowed pines and the sheep-bells' clamour,*
   *The wet, lit lane and the yellow-hammer,*
   *The orchard and the chaffinch song,*
   *Only to the Brave belong.*

L

*And he shall lose their joy for aye*
*If their price he cannot pay,*
*Who shall find them dearer far*
*Enriched by blood after long War.'*

ROBERT NICHOLS.

# The South Country

WHEN I am living in the Midlands
  That are sodden and unkind,
I light my lamp in the evening:
  My work is left behind;
And the great hills of the South Country
  Come back into my mind.

The great hills of the South Country
  They stand along the sea,
And it 's there walking in the high woods
  That I could wish to be,
And the men that were boys when I was a boy
  Walking along with me.

The men that live in North England
  I saw them for a day:
Their hearts are set upon the waste fells,
  Their skies are fast and grey;
From their castle-walls a man may see
  The mountains far away.

The men that live in West England
  They see the Severn strong,
A-rolling on rough water brown
  Light aspen leaves along.
They have the secret of the Rocks,
  And the oldest kind of song.

But the men that live in the South Country
 Are the kindest and most wise,
They get their laughter from the loud surf,
 And the faith in their happy eyes
Comes surely from our Sister the Spring
 When over the sea she flies;
The violets suddenly bloom at her feet,
 She blesses us with surprise.

I never get between the pines
 But I smell the Sussex air;
Nor I never come on a belt of sand
 But my home is there.
And along the sky the line of the Downs
 So noble and so bare.

A lost thing could I never find,
 Nor a broken thing mend:
And I fear I shall be all alone
 When I get towards the end.
Who will there be to comfort me
 Or who will be my friend?

I will gather and carefully make my friends
 Of the men of the Sussex Weald,
They watch the stars from silent folds,
 They stiffly plough the field.
By them and the God of the South Country
 My poor soul shall be healed.

If I ever become a rich man,
 Or if ever I grow to be old,
I will build a house with deep thatch
 To shelter me from the cold,
And there shall the Sussex songs be sung
 And the story of Sussex told.

I will hold my house in the high wood
  Within a walk of the sea,
And the men that were boys when I was a boy
  Shall sit and drink with me.

HILAIRE BELLOC.

# English Country Towns

THAT there may be more picturesqueness in an old German, Italian, and French town may be admitted, but it is of a more salient, obtrusive character than that which exists in our old country towns. The continental architects aimed at bold effects. I do not say that they were wrong. They achieved great success. Our architects built what was wanted, in a quiet undemonstrative manner, and left effect to chance, and chance gave what they did not seek. The charms of an old English country town do not force themselves on our notice, are missed altogether by the hasty visitor; they have to be found out, they come by surprises, they depend on certain lights and plays of shadow, on the bursting into leaf of certain trees, on the setting up of certain hucksters' stalls. That a great deal of their picturesqueness is passing away is, alas! only too true. The tradesmen want huge window spaces for the display of their goods, so away is knocked the quaint old frontage of the house, and is replaced by something that can be sustained on iron supports between wide sheets of plate-glass. The suburbs are being made hideous with rows of model cottages, all precisely alike, roofed with blue slate. Nevertheless a great deal remains, and it is fortunately now something like a fashion to give us Queen Anne (so-called) gables in the streets, which at all events afford a pretty broken sky-line, and a play of light and shade on the frontage.

Then how different are the outskirts of a foreign town to

an English country town. In Italy there are miles of lanes between high stone walls, over which indeed lemons show their glorious fruit and blaze in the sun; nevertheless, the sorry fact remains, that for as far as one cares to walk there is no prospect save by favour through a gate.

At Florence, for instance, it is wall, wall, on the right hand and on the left, all the way to Fiesole; and to the south, beyond S. Miniato, up and down the hills, wall, wall, on the right hand and on the left. At Genoa the city is engirded with hills, indeed the town lies in a crater, broken down to the west to the sea. Climb near two thousand feet to the encircling fortresses, and you go between wall, wall, all the way. And a French town or a German town, or a Belgian town, starts up suddenly out of bare fields, without trees, without hedges, with a suburb of tall, hideous, stuccoed badly-built houses, all precisely alike and equally ugly. There are no cottages. Come back to England, and at once you discover that the cottage is that which gives charm to the approach of a town, it is the moss, the lichen that adheres to the wall, a softening, beautiful feature in itself. Then there are our hedges and hedgerow trees, and how different from the stiff avenues of poplar, and the boulevards of set planes, exactly ten paces apart.

S. BARING-GOULD, *Old Country Life*.

# A Refrain

TELL the tune his feet beat
On the ground all day—
Black-burnt ground and green grass
Seamed with rocks of grey—
'England,' 'England,' 'England,'
That one word they say.
Now they tread the beech-mast,

Now the ploughland's clay,
Now the faery ball-floor of her fields in May.
Now her red June sorrel, now her new-turned hay,
Now they keep the great road, now by sheep-path stray,
Still it 's 'England,' 'England,'
'England' all the way!

A. S. CRIPPS.

# England

We have no grass locked up in ice so fast
That cattle cut their faces and at last,
When it is reached, must lie them down and starve,
With bleeding mouths that freeze too hard to move.
We have not that delirious state of cold
That makes men warm and sing when in Death's hold.
We have no roaring floods whose angry shocks
Can kill the fishes dashed against their rocks.
We have no winds that cut down street by street
As easy as our scythes can cut down wheat.
No mountains here to spew their burning hearts
Into the valleys, on our human parts.
No earthquakes here, that ring church bells afar,
A hundred miles from where those earthquakes are.
We have no cause to set our dreaming eyes,
Like Arabs, on fresh streams in Paradise.
We have no wilds to harbour men that tell
More murders than they can remember well.
No woman here shall wake from her night's rest,
To find a snake is sucking at her breast.
Though I have travelled many and many a mile,
And had a man to clean my boots and smile
With teeth that had less bone in them than gold—
Give me this England now for all my world.

W. H. DAVIES, Collected Poems.

# In Memoriam: an Unknown Warrior

HE was a boy bred of the fields of Ouse;
  At manhood's dawn they called him, and he went;
Having the beauty of the world to lose,
  All that he had, he spent.

What things of joy were his in those few days
  Of promise in Cromwellian pastures known;
The reedy levels of the river-ways,
  Great meadows freshly mown.

Sometimes at twilight, when his wage was won,
  Upon the bridge of Hinching Brook he'd stand,
Looking across the peace of Huntingdon,
  His own secluded land.

And he would count the lilies of the stream,
  Swing from a weedy bed on slender stalks,
And see the plumes of the kingfisher gleam
  Along the chestnut walks.

Under the willows, where the water lay
  So still that in its glass the spinning flies
Were mirrored in their slight ephemeral play,
  He saw the sleek chub rise,

And, passing home, his handkerchief he'd fill
  With silver-padded mushrooms, that he found
In lace of grassy fetters binding still
  Their whiteness to the ground.

Or by the hedges he would walk at ease,
  Where berries ripened from the bramble root,
Or make the branches of crab apple trees
  Tumble their yellowing fruit.

And, husht across the sky twixt day and dark,
  To her far nest high folded in the night,
The fisher heron from her pools he 'd mark
  In solitary flight.

Nightfall; and foxes barking from the copse,
  The little owls crying upon their prey;
The drowsy pheasants in the cedar-tops;
  And so, the end of day.

And, bidden from this dear tranquillity
  Where Ouse among her milk and honey flows,
Sudden be passed, our singing boy, to be
  An anger among foes.

He went, and going made a broken end
  Of love, of beauty, all fair things and well;
For us he made it; and we call him friend,
  And have no more to tell.

He and a million brothers. By that sleep,
  Be silence and thanksgiving reconciled,
Silence in all, save in the will to keep
  His England undefiled.

JOHN DRINKWATER, *Collected Poems*.

# English Reverie

ALL through the morning, the air was held in an ominous stillness. Sitting over my books, I seemed to feel the silence; when I turned my look to the window, I saw nothing but the broad, grey sky, a featureless expanse, cold, melancholy. Later, just as I was bestirring myself to go out for an afternoon walk, something white fell softly across my vision. A few minutes more, and all was hidden with a descending veil of silent snow.

It is a disappointment. Yesterday I half believed that the winter drew to its end; the breath of the hills was soft; spaces of limpid azure shone amid slow-drifting clouds, and seemed the promise of spring. Idle by the fireside, in the gathering dusk, I began to long for the days of light and warmth. My fancy wandered, leading me far and wide in a dream of summer England. . . .

This is the valley of the Blythe. The stream ripples and glances over its brown bed warmed with sunbeams; by its bank the green flags wave and rustle, and, all about, the meadows shine in pure gold of buttercups. The hawthorn hedges are a mass of gleaming blossom which scents the breeze. There above rises the heath, yellow-mantled with gorse, and beyond, if I walk for an hour or two, I shall come out upon the sandy cliffs of Suffolk, and look over the northern sea. . . .

I ramble through a village in Gloucestershire, a village which seems forsaken in this drowsy warmth of the afternoon. The houses of grey stone are old and beautiful, telling of a time when Englishmen knew how to build whether for rich or poor; the gardens glow with flowers, and the air is delicately sweet. At the village end, I come into a lane, which winds upwards between grassy slopes, to turf and bracken and woods of noble beech. Here I am upon a spur of the Cotswolds, and before me spreads the wide vale of Evesham, with its ripening crops, its fruiting orchards, watered by sacred Avon. Beyond, softly blue, the hills of Malvern. On the branch hard by warbles a little bird, glad in his leafy solitude. A rabbit jumps through the fern. Then sounds the laugh of a woodpecker from the copse in yonder hollow. . . .

A pathway leads me by the winding of the river Ouse. Far on every side stretches a homely landscape, tilth and pasture, hedgerow and clustered trees, to where the sky rests upon the gentle hills. Slow, silent, the river lapses between its daisied banks, its grey-green osier beds. Yonder is the little town of St Neots. In all England no simpler bit of rural scenery; in all the world nothing of its kind more beautiful. Cattle are lowing amid the rich meadows. Here one may loiter and dream in utter restfulness, whilst the great white clouds mirror themselves in the water as they pass above. . . .

I am walking upon the South Downs. In the valleys, the sun lies hot, but here sings a breeze which freshens the forehead and fills the heart with gladness. My foot upon the short, soft turf has an unwearied lightness; I feel capable of walking on and on, even to that farthest horizon where the white cloud casts its floating shadow. Below me, but far off, is the summer sea, still, silent, its ever-changing blue and green dimmed at the long limit with luminous noontide mist. Inland spreads the undulant vastness of the sheep-spotted downs, beyond them the tillage and the woods of Sussex weald, coloured like to the pure sky above them, but in deeper tint. Near by, all but hidden among trees in yon lovely hollow, lies an old, old hamlet, its brown roofs decked with golden lichen; I see the low church-tower, and the little graveyard about it. Meanwhile high in the heaven, a lark is singing. It descends; it drops to its nest and I could dream that half the happiness of its exultant song was love of England. . . .

GEORGE GISSING. *The Private Papers of Henry Ryecroft.*

# Market Day

THE street that past my window runs
  Links up the country with the town,
And all the world on market day
  Along my street goes up and down.

The great farm horses, clip-a-clop,
  Tossing their heads and stepping slow,
With coloured favours in the manes
  From bondage into bondage go;

Their glossy coats give back the sun,
  Their minds are packed with memories
Of master-voices, rustling stalls,
  The brown land naked to the skies;

And now a pattering flock of sheep
  Swarm by in huddled mute distress,
And shut the traffic down, and break
  Their drivers' hearts with foolishness;

And market carts from dawn to dusk
  Come clattering down the cobbled street,
With fruits and vegetables fresh
  With dew, and children country-sweet

Dreaming upon the dirty straw,
  Or watching city chimneys smoke,
With deep behind their restless eyes
  The quietude of rustic folk.

                              P. H. B. LYON.

BIBURY, GLOUCESTERSHIRE]

# Travelling

'PECKHAM RYE, Loughborough, Elephant, St Paul's,'
Every morning the porter bawls,
The train grinds out . . . and I gaze on lots
Of sad back gardens and chimney-pots,
Factory stacks and smoky haze
Showering smuts on the close-packed ways.
And the train jolts on and twists and crawls. . . .
'Peckham Rye, Loughborough, Elephant, St Paul's.'

But, trapped and prisoned as I may be,
I lift a latch and my thoughts go free,
And once again I am running down
On a winding track from a Cornish town,
And I dream the names of the stations through—
'Moorswater, Causeland, Sandplace, Looe.'

An ancient engine with puff nigh gone
Drags a couple of coaches on
Close where a stream runs all the way
Muttering music night and day;
There isn't a porter about at all
To spoil the peace with a raucous bawl,
But a kind old guard to see me through,
Give me a ticket, and take it too.
The line twists down through patches sweet
Of soft green pasture and waving wheat
And the stream spreads out to a river wide
Where ships creep up at the turn of tide,
Till a tangle of spars on a blue sky spun
Gives me the sign of the journey done,
And I stand contented on the quay
And hear the surging song of the sea.

So runs the dreamlike journey through,
'Moorswater, Causeland, Sandplace, Looe';—
But every morning the porter bawls,
'Peckham Rye, Loughborough, Elephant, St Paul's.'

BERNARD MOORE, *A Cornish Chorus.*

# What is England?

IN the spring of 1923 I believed that I was dying in Palestine. There was no woman at hand to convince me that the pain in my neck was not the first sign of spinal meningitis, so that, growing rapidly worse, I began to attend my own funeral every day. My appetite, however, remained excellent.

In the black depths of misery, I climbed a hill overlooking Jerusalem, unaffected by the fact that this has been considered the best of all places to die, and, turning as accurately as I could in the direction of England, I gave way to such a wave of home sickness that almost shames me now when I recollect it. I find it impossible in cold blood, and at this distance, to put into words the longing that shook me. I have forgotten the pain in the neck but I shall never forget the pain in the heart.

As I looked out over the inhospitable mountains I remembered home in a way which given any other frame of mind would have astonished me. I solemnly cursed every moment I had spent wandering foolishly about the world, and I swore that if ever I saw Dover cliffs again I would never leave them. I had by this time made myself too ill to realize that it is this rare stay-at-home sanity which justifies travel. Perhaps in instinctive contrast to the cold, unhappy, mountains of Palestine there rose up in my mind the picture of a village street at dusk with a smell of wood smoke lying in the still air and, here and there, little red blinds shining in the dusk under the thatch. I remembered how the church bells ring at home, and how, at that time of year, the sun leaves a dull red bar low down in the west, and against it the elms grow blacker every minute. Then the bats start to flicker like little bits of burnt paper and you hear the slow jingle of a team coming home from fields. . . . When you think like this sitting alone in a foreign country I think you know all there is to learn about heartache.

But does it seem strange that a townsman should in his extremity see this picture? Would it not be more reasonable to expect him to see his own city? Why did I not think of St Paul's Cathedral or Piccadilly? I have learnt since that this vision of mine is a common one to exiles all over the world: we think of home, we long for home, but we see something greater—*we see England.*

This village that symbolizes England sleeps in the subconsciousness of many a townsman. A little London factory hand whom I met during the war confessed to me when pressed, and after great mental difficulty, that he visualized the England he was fighting for—the England of the 'England wants you' poster—not as London, not his own street, but as Epping Forest, the green place where he had spent bank holidays. And I think most of us did. The village and the English countryside are the germs of all we are and all we have become: our manufacturing cities belong to the last century and a half; our villages stand with their roots in the Heptarchy.

I was humiliated, mourning there above Jerusalem, to realize how little I knew about England. I was shamed to think that I had wandered so far and so often over the world neglecting those lovely things near at home, feeling that England would always be there whenever I wanted to see her; and at that moment how far away she seemed, how unattainable! I took a vow that if my pain in the neck did not end for ever on the windy hills of Palestine I would go home in search of England, I would go through the lanes of

England and the little thatched villages of England, and I
would lean over English bridges and lie on English grass
watching an English sky.

H. V. MORTON, *In Search of England.*


# The Return of the Home-Born

All along the white chalk coast
    The mist lifts clear.
Wight is glimmering like a ghost.
    The ship draws near.
Little inch-wide meadows
    Lost so many a day,
The first time I knew you
    Was when I turned away.

Island—little island—
    Lost so many a year,
Mother of all I leave behind
    —*Draw me near!*—
Mother of half the rolling world,
    And O, so little and gray,
The first time I found you
    Was when I turned away.

*Over yon green water*
    *Sussex lies.*
*But the slow mists gather*
    *In our eyes.*
*England, little island*
    *—God, how dear!—*
*Fold me in your mighty arms,*
    *Draw me near.*

Little tawny roofs of home,
  Nestling in the gray,
Where the smell of Sussex loam
  Blows across the bay. . . .
Fold me, teach me, draw me close,
  Lest in death I say
The first time I loved you
  Was when I turned away.

ALFRED NOYES, *Collected Poems.*

# 9. Epilogue

# Britain is in Danger

AT the beginning of this book, I said that the England that the great water-colour artists had painted, round about 1800, had not then been spoilt. If you look at old drawings and paintings of our country, you will notice that you rarely see anything ugly or strikingly inharmonious in them. In the seventeenth or eighteenth centuries, this island, though not always very comfortable to live in, must have been quite exceptionally attractive to the eye. Not only had we a most charmingly varied, green countryside, bright with flowers in spring and early summer, rich with yellowing woods in autumn; but we had several equally attractive styles of domestic architecture. Moreover, the eighteenth century especially was the period of our great craftsmen in furniture. In those days, almost everything you bought was well made and pretty to look at. Towards the end of the century, what is called the Industrial Revolution, which turned Britain from an agricultural into a mining and manufacturing country, was in full swing, but there had not been time to turn whole regions of what had once been pleasant countryside into black and desolate tracts, like those we still see in the Black Country, Lancashire, the West Riding, Durham, and the Tyne. No, everything was still as you see in the old prints and pictures, almost like a country in a fairy-tale.

Then came the spoiling, which has been done with such terrible thoroughness that everybody who really cares tuppence about our country is now greatly alarmed about it all. There are two main attacks of spoiling: the nineteenth and the twentieth century. You can see the results of the nineteenth-century attack in any industrial district:

blackened fields, slag heaps, hills torn open, gloomy and dirty factories, messy railway sidings, stinking canals, and rows and rows of poky little houses all looking exactly alike and with nothing attractive about them. This happened long ago, and it is not so important now as the second great attack, the twentieth-century one, which is *still going on*. And I believe this to be the worse of the two, because although the first spoiling did completely ruin the look of certain districts, usually the ones where there was coal or iron, it left whole counties, where there was nothing to be torn out of the ground, more or less as it found them, so that much of the old Britain still looked the same. You had only to get out of the manufacturing areas to find some lovely country and lots of unspoilt market towns and delightful villages. When I was a boy, I lived in a rather ugly town, Bradford, in the West Riding of Yorkshire, but a tram ride and then an hour or two's walking took me to beautiful, unspoilt country, where you would never think there was a manufacturing town within a hundred miles. And because working on the land did not pay very well and there was plenty of work in the new factories, the people of a hundred years ago all began to move into the towns. Also, the railways came, and the old coach roads were now deserted, and people moved to be near railway stations. Thus, when we read Victorian authors like Dickens, Thackeray, Trollope, Mrs Gaskell, we realize that though the towns must have been horrible, worse than many towns now, the country must still have been quite charming, much as it was a hundred years before.

Our twentieth-century spoiling, especially our nineteen-twenty, nineteen-thirty spoiling, has been much worse, however, because instead of concentrating the nasty attack on a few districts, it has set to work to ruin the look of the whole island. Then you could escape from the nasty mess we were making of our country. Now there is hardly any escape. Everywhere you go, you notice the same carelessness and nastiness and stupidity. The fairy-tale place has almost gone, only bits of it, as I said at the beginning of this book, surviving to remind us, to reproach us. Why is it that we have made such a mess of things? Are we worse than our grandfathers were? No, I do not really think we are, but circumstances so far have been too much for us. The truth is, we cannot any longer allow people to do just as they please, but we shall have to make definite plans and to lay down rules that must not be broken.

Here are some reasons why the spoiling has been so much worse during the last twenty years. First, just as the railways kept people near their stations, so the evolution of the motor car and the development of road transport have spread people out again. That in itself is not a bad thing and might even be a good one, if we had not allowed people to do as they liked and make everything higgledy-piggledy. This is what happens, over and over again. Because there are so many motor vehicles, from heavy lorries to small private cars, going in and out of a city, we construct a specially broad and straight road, and call it an arterial road or a bypass. It is not pleasant to look at (though it can be, if you plant trees at each side of it, as they have done along many main roads in the United States), and it goes smashing its way across the landscape, clean through what were once fields and woods; but it will take care of all the heavy traffic. As soon as the road is finished, however, firms of builders buy the land on each side of the road, and begin hastily throwing up hundreds of bungalows and the like, shops and garages and cinemas, so that very soon the road that was made specially to escape the town has now become a sort of town itself, which was the very last thing that was originally intended. This is called *Ribbon Development*, and it is going on all over England. It is no good to anybody, except the people who sell the new houses that have been built. The town, instead of stopping properly and giving the meadows and woods a chance, now straggles on mile after mile. The new houses and shops look a mess. The road is more congested with traffic than before. And some nice bit of the real England has gone for ever. If you live in that town and want to go for a walk in the fields, you have now so much further to go, because of this ugly ribbon development, that you may give it up in disgust. And the fields you might have played football or hockey in are now miles away.

Then again, when factories had to be worked by steam engines, nearly all the factories were concentrated in the districts where there was plenty of cheap coal. But now, when so many factories use electric power, which can be run out to almost any place, you are liable to find a factory anywhere. I admit that some of the factories look much better than the big, gloomy old ones did. But you do not want to find them round every corner. I am not one of those people who dislike towns. I was brought up in one, and I do not mind town life at all. It is pleasant to meet all manner of folk, to have big shops, libraries, art galleries, theatres, concert halls, cinemas, football matches, and the rest. I like towns, which can be really handsome if they are properly designed and built and kept clean and are not just a nasty dark mess. I also like the country, with its fields and hedges, streams and woods, hills and moors. But what I do not like is something that is neither town nor country, a stupid half-and-half, that cannot settle down and be really urban and yet is completely spoilt as country. Now more and more of this island is being turned into this unpleasant half-and-half, neither town nor country, and if we do not stop it, we shall soon say good-bye for ever to the lovely country our forefathers knew. It is very agreeable to possess a motor car so that you can pop into it and go where you like, but if there are so many of you going about in motor cars and everywhere ugly garages and tea-shops and cinemas and dance-halls are being built for you, and where it used to be quiet there is now a constant din,

[THE GREAT WEST ROAD, 1924 AND 1931

then obviously there is no sense in going anywhere because there is really *nowhere to go*. Whatever place you arrive at looks just as bad and makes the same silly noise as the place you started from, so that nobody enjoys a real change.

Another reason why the country is beginning to look so ugly is that now, having so many different building materials to choose from, we are apt to choose the wrong one. In the old days, when it was expensive and difficult to transport building material a long way, you used whatever you could find in the district. Thus, in some parts of the country the houses would be built of stone, in others brick, in others they would be half-timbered, in others the cottages would be thatched. Now it is a well-known fact that the local material always looks right against the landscape. It fits in perfectly because it has come out of that district. Against the sombre background of the moors of the West Riding, for example, the local, rather dark stone is absolutely right. In the Cotswolds, their grey stone makes everything look beautifully harmonious. In other districts, red brick is completely in place. But now everything is hideously mixed up. Builders often set to work with what is cheapest, no matter where it comes from or how it looks. One of my favourite views, a long grey-and-green vista in Wharfedale, is now ruined because bang in the middle of it some insensitive donkey of a builder has erected some bright-red bungalows, which look as much in place as a thatched cottage would in Greenland. Now this too is happening everywhere, and the old harmony of our countryside is rapidly being turned into a screaming discord. You may think this is a great deal of fuss about nothing, but really it is even more important than I have suggested yet, because when everything looks wrong, tasteless, foolish, and downright ugly, the people who have to live in these places begin to feel wrong themselves. Our old poets and essayists and novelists could praise their country and feel proud of it because it constantly offered them visions of beauty; but if everything is to be stupid, silly, and ugly, such a country can hardly be loved and praised.

I am not one of those people who believe that everything old is good and everything new is bad. As a matter of fact, new buildings, new furniture, new curtains, crockery, glasses, can be extremely charming. We are just as capable as our forefathers were of making everything about us look attractive, *when we take the trouble*. But as a rule we do not take the trouble. We imagine anything will do. We allow men to pull down beautiful old buildings to put in their place ugly new ones, whereas we ought to insist that every new building is an improvement on what was there before. Instead of scattering higgledy-piggledy bungalows all over the landscape, as if a giant had shaken them out of a pepper-pot, we ought to ask good architects to design for us squares, terraces, and crescents, which are actually cheaper to build and much nicer to look at. We ought to put a stop to this ribbon development, improve our existing towns instead of ruining more and more countryside. We ought to insist that beautiful parts of the countryside are treated with care, as if they were precious, and not daubed over with ridiculous advertisements, made hideous with petrol pumps and teashop signs, buried deep in litter, and turned into a fairground. The War Office and Air Ministry may need more and more space for encampments, landing grounds, ranges, and the like, but there is no reason why time after time they should single out some of the few unspoilt regions in the country, to ruin them for ever.

The easiest thing in the world is to spoil. One wandering hippopotamus can wreck an African garden in five minutes. Destruction is easy and swift; creation is long and hard. It took centuries of honest workmanship and loving craftsmanship to create the England that was renowned for its charm and delicate beauty. In twenty years we have completely ruined at least half that England. This must not go on. We cannot spend all our lives in what is beginning to look like a fairground after a Bank Holiday. It is even more your concern now than ours, for you have more of your life in front of you than we, who are much older, have. This country is your inheritance. Just imagine that you knew you were going to inherit a magnificent piano, a really famous instrument, the very best of its kind, and that suddenly you learned that not only was it not being kept clean and properly tuned but that the people in charge of it were now chopping off bits of the case for firewood and using the inside of the instrument as a dustbin. You would be extremely hurt and annoyed. Now this island is your inheritance, and people are behaving as badly towards it as the imaginary folks did towards the piano. Unless all of us, young and old, make up our minds to banish messiness and ugliness, agree that all future building must be carefully planned and that the countryside must not be ruined by anybody's foolishness or greed, and take care that nothing we do ourselves, even if it is only throwing orange peel about at a picnic, shall contribute to the general vandalism, the beautiful isle of Britain that has been praised by so many great men will be nothing but a fading memory.

J. B. Priestley.

# Acknowledgments

For permission to quote the copyright material thanks are due to—

THE Automobile Association for 'Decline of the English Inn,' from *This Motoring*, by Sir Stenson Cooke; Basil Blackwell for 'A Refrain' by A. S. Cripps; William Blackwood & Sons, Ltd, and Alfred Noyes for 'The Return of the Home-Born' and the lines from 'The Barrel Organ' from *The Collected Poems of Alfred Noyes*; Burns, Oates, & Washbourne, Ltd, for 'The Escape' from *The Story of Ben-Ban* by A. M. M. Hales; Jonathan Cape, Ltd, for 'England' and 'Winter's Beauty' from *Collected Poems* by W. H. Davies; Chapman & Hall, Ltd, for 'The Broads' from *East Anglia* by R. H. Mottram; The Clarendon Press, Oxford, for 'The Winnowers' from *The Shorter Poems of Robert Bridges* (1931); Chatto & Windus for 'The Ploughing Lesson' from *Down in the Valley* by H. W. Freeman; R. Cobden Sanderson, Ltd, for 'Winter: East Anglia' and 'The Idlers' from *Poems 1914-30* and 'A Yeoman' from *English Poems* by Edmund Blunden; Constable & Co., Ltd, for 'English Reverie' from *The Private Papers of Henry Ryecroft* by George Gissing and 'Market Day' by P. H. B. Lyon; J. M. Dent & Sons, Ltd, for 'Sutton Club Walking' from *English Country Life* by Walter Raymond, 'Abuse of the Countryside' from *The South Country* by Edward Thomas, 'The White Owl' from *Nature in Downland* by W. H. Hudson, 'A Cold Day at Silchester' from *Afoot in England* by W. H. Hudson, and 'Planting a Spinney' from *Alpha of the Plough* (*2nd Series*); Gerald Duckworth & Co., Ltd, and Mr Belloc for 'The South Country,' and Gerald Duckworth for 'An Old Labourer' from *The Bettesworth Book* by George Bourne; Faber & Faber, Ltd, for 'The Spacious Days' from *Farmer's Glory* by A. G. Street; William Heinemann, Ltd, and Mr Francis Brett Young (The Vice-chairman of the Council for the Preservation of

## 172 ACKNOWLEDGMENTS

Rural England for Worcestershire) for 'Mr Jagger' from *Portrait of a Village*, and William Heinemann for 'The Cotswolds' from *English Journey* by J. B. Priestley; Hodder & Stoughton, Ltd, and Lord Mottistone (J. B. Seely) for 'The Blacksmith' from *For Ever England*; Longmans Green & Co., Ltd, for 'Pre-war Country' from *The Face of England* by Edmund Blunden, 'The Brook' from *Wood Magic* by Richard Jefferies, and 'A Boy's Game' from *Cricket* by Neville Cardus; Macmillan & Co., Ltd, and the Executors of Thomas Hardy for 'The Reddleman' from *The Return of the Native* and 'In Time of "The Breaking of Nations"' from *Collected Poems of Thomas Hardy*; Macmillan & Co., Ltd, for 'The Lily-pool' and 'For J. P.' from *Collected Poems of T. E. Brown*; Methuen & Co., Ltd, for 'On the River' from *The Wind in the Willows* by Kenneth Grahame, 'English Country Towns' from *Old Country Life* by S. Baring-Gould, 'Miner' from *Our Fellow Men* by H. V. Morton, 'What is England?' and 'York' from *In Search of England* by H. V. Morton, 'The Mowing of a Field' from *Hills and the Sea* by Hilaire Belloc, and Methuen & Co., Ltd, and Mr Robert Lynd for 'Picking Flowers' from *It's a Fine World*; James Nisbet & Co., Ltd, and Mr Anthony Collett for 'Ancient Trackways' from *The Changing Face of England*; Rich & Cowan, Ltd, for 'Trees' from *A Cottage in the Country* by Reginald Arkell; Sidgwick & Jackson, Ltd, and the author's representatives for 'In Memoriam: an Unknown Warrior' from *Collected Poems* by John Drinkwater; *The Times* for 'The Curse of Litter' by Edward Grey (Viscount Grey of Falloden) from *The Open Air Year*; Williams & Norgate, Ltd, for 'The Carrier' from *Village Idylls* by S. L. Bensusan.

Mr Rex Welldon Finn for 'The English Roads' from *The English Heritage*; Mr John Masefield for 'The Drive in the Snowstorm' from *The Hawbucks* (William Heinemann, Ltd); the Executors of the late C. E. Montague for 'On Knowing a Country' from *The Right Place*; Mr Bernard Moore for 'Travelling' from *A Cornish Chorus*; Mr Robert Nichols for 'At the Wars.'